# Exploring Geography in a
# Changing World

## Simon Ross

**HODDER**
EDUCATION
PART OF HACHETTE LIVRE UK

Orders: please contact Bookpoint Ltd, 130 Milton Park, Abingdon, Oxon OX14 4SB. Telephone: (44) 01235 827720. Fax: (44) 01235 400454. Lines are open 9.00–5.00, Monday to Saturday, with a 24-hour message answering service. Visit our website at www.hoddereducation.co.uk

© Simon Ross 2008
First published in 2008 by
Hodder Education
Part of Hachette Livre UK
338 Euston Road
London NW1 3BH

Impression number    5    4    3    2    1
Year                                2012   2011   2010   2009   2008

Cover photo Martin Bennett/Reuters/Corbis
Illustrations by Barking Dog Art
Typeset in New Baskerville 11.5/13pt
Layouts by Amanda Easter

A catalogue record for this title is available from the British Library

ISBN-13: 978 0340 946 077

**Other titles in the series:**

Year 7 Pupil's Book: 978 0340 94607 7
Teacher's Resource Book: 978 0340 96973 1
Dynamic Learning Network Edition CD-ROM: 978 0340 94778 4

Year 8 Pupil's Book: 978 0340 94605 3
Teacher's Resource Book: 978 0340 97294 6
Dynamic Learning Network Edition CD-ROM: 978 0340 94779 1

Year 9 Pupil's Book: 978 0340 946 06 0
Teacher's Resource Book: 978 0340 97295 3
Dynamic Learning Network Edition CD-ROM: 978 0340 94780 7

# CONTENTS

Introduction    1

**Chapter 1**    My Home Environment    11

Chapter 2    Ordnance Survey Map Skills    21

**Chapter 3**    Weather and Climate    35

**Chapter 4**    The Physical Landscape    49

**Chapter 5**    River Landscapes    59

**Chapter 6**    People    71

**Chapter 7**    Settlement    83

**Chapter 8**    Farming and Industry    95

**Chapter 9**    Energy    105

**Chapter 10**    Leisure and Recreation    113

**Chapter 11**    Environment    125

**Glossary**    135

**Index**    139

# Acknowledgements

This book is dedicated to our much-loved Aunt Joan whose tremendous wisdom and energy has been an inspiration to us all.

I would like to thank the following individuals and organisation for their help in the preparation of this book:

Mackie's Ice Cream (especially Karin Hayhow and Nikki Nangle); Jill and Ronald Russell; William Fish; Helen Sail; Gyles Morris, for some of his creative ideas about fieldwork opportunities; RSPB; Polly Mitchell; Monty Stand; Joan Carmichael and Peter Jeevar; Berkhamsted Collegiate School; Great Tooting in the Marsh Gas Recycling Initiative; River Restoration Centre; Kim and Augustus Tasse; Jerry Adesanmi; Visit Blackpool.

I am extremely grateful to Jenny Fitzgerald, Ruth Lowe, Vicki Taylor and Dave Holmes for all the hard work that they have put into this project. I would also like to thank numerous pupils at Queen's College, Taunton for providing me (unknowingly!) with inspiration and constructive feedback.

Last but not least I would like to thank my wife Nikki and children Susi and James for their continuing support, energetic whooping and patient acceptance of my need to barricade myself into my study for long periods of time. Particular thanks are due to James who, not only helped with the collection of material, but also acted as a much-valued 'guinea pig'.

The Publishers would like to thank the following for permission to reproduce their copyright material:

**Photo credits:**
**p.1** European Space Agency; **p.2** Johnson Space Center/NASA; **p.3** *t* Simon Ross, *b* Simon Ross; **p.4** John Peter Photography/Alamy; **p.5** Gideon Mendel/Corbis; **p.6** *l* The Print Collector/Alamy; **p.10** Nikreates/Alamy; **p.11** Peter Brown/Alamy; **p.12** *l* Hamish Blair/Getty Images, *r* Denny Rowland/Alamy; **p.14** *tl* Tim Graham/Alamy, *tr* Richard Osbourne/Blue Pearl Photographic/Alamy, *bl* Chris Howes/Wild Places Photography/Alamy, *br* South West Images Scotland/Alamy; **p.15** Peter Barritt/Alamy; **p.16** Simon Ross; **p.19** Mark Boulton/Alamy; **p.21** RESO/Rex Features; **p.26** © Ant Strack/Corbis; **p.33** *t* Simon Ross, *b* Getmapping.plc; **p.34** Andrew Holt/Alamy; **p.35** Richard Austin/Rex Features; **p.36** *t* PA Photos/Jeff Moore, *m* Andrew Fox/Alamy, *b* Neil McAllister/Alamy; **p.37** Berndt-Joel Gunnarsson/Nordic Photos/Getty Images; **p.40** *t* Rex Features, *ml* Rex Features, *mr* David White/Alamy, *b* © The Art Archive/Corbis; **p.41** *b* Scott Aiken/Rex Features; **p.42** *l* Tyson Benton/Getty Images, *r* Barry Batchelor/PA Photos; **p.43** Simon Ross; **p.46** Travstock/Alamy; **p.49** nagelestock.com/Alamy; **p.50** *t* Roger Bamber/Alamy, *m* Alan Novelli/Alamy, *b* Worldwide Picture Library/Alamy; **p.52** *l* Simon Ross, *r* Jon Sparks/Alamy; **p.53** *tl* David Noton Photography/Alamy, *tr* imagebroker/Alamy, *b* Simon Ross; **p.54** Simon Ross; **p.55** *t* Paul Heaton/Alamy, *b* Michael Jenner/Alamy; **p.57** *t* Leslie Garland Picture Library/Alamy; **p.58** david martyn hughes/Alamy; **p.59** Paul Glendell/Alamy; **p.60** Simon Ross; **p.61** *t* Simon Ross, *ml* Simon Ross, *mr* © Coaster/Alamy, *br* © Bob Croxford/www.atmosphere.co.uk, *bl* © Bob Croxford/www.atmosphere.co.uk; **p.62** Simon Ross; **p.63** © Bob Croxford/ www.atmosphere.co.uk; **p.64** Simon Ross; **p.65** © Coaster/Alamy; **p.66** © Bob Croxford/www.atmosphere.co.uk, **p.69** *l*, *r* River Restoration Centre; **p.70** © Martin de Retuerto, Wessex Chalk Streams Project/Courtesy of the River Restoration Centre; **p.71** Photofusion Picture Library/Alamy; **p.72** Simon Ross; **p.76** Tony Cortazzi/Alamy; **p.77** *l* Kevin Allen/Alamy, *r* Topical Press Agency/ Getty Images; **p.78** *t* FLPA/Alamy, *ml* imagebroker/Alamy, *mr* UpperCut Images/Alamy, *bl* Jack Sullivan/Alamy, *br* Rex Features; **p.79** David Burton/Alamy; **p.80** Christopher Pillitz/Alamy; **p.81** Nick Hanna/ Alamy; **p.82** Jenny Fitzgerald; **p.83** David Hoffman Photo Library/ Alamy; **p.84** *t* Cotswolds Photo Library/Alamy, *bl* © webbaviation.co.uk, *br* © webbaviation.co.uk; **p.89** London 2012; **p.90** *bl* Richard Watson/ Alamy, *tr* © London Wildlife Trust – Camley Street Natural Park; **p.92** *t* Colin Underhill/Alamy, *bl* Alisdair Macdonald/Rex Features, *m* Sam Toren/Alamy, *br* LOOK Die Bildagentur der Fotografen GmbH/ Alamy; **p.95** imagestopshop/Alamy; **p.96** *l* Adrian Sherratt/Alamy, *m* Martin Jenkinson/Alamy, *r* Ian Miles-Flashpoint Pictures/Alamy; **p.97** © Mackie's of Scotland; **p.98** © Mackie's of Scotland; **p.99** *t* © Mackie's of Scotland, *m* © Mackie's of Scotland, *b* © Mackie's of Scotland; **p.100** *t* © Bob Krist/CORBIS; **p.101** *all* © Mackie's of Scotland; **p.102** © *insert* Mackie's of Scotland; **p.103** Organic Picture Library/ Rex Features; **p.104** Alan Curtis/Alamy; **p.105** Edward Parker/Alamy; **p.106** Ian M Butterfield/Alamy; **p.107** *t* © CHRIS JAMES/Still Pictures, *b* © Leeds Museums and Art Galleries (City Museum) UK/The Bridgeman Art Library; **p.108** Vincent Lowe/Alamy; **p.109** *l* Paul Shearman/Alamy, *r* © Mackie's of Scotland; **p.110** Modern Architecture and Construction – Paul White/Alamy; **p.113** Images Etc Ltd/Alamy; **p.114** 2007 Mike Goldwater/Alamy; **p.116** *t* The Photolibrary Wales/ Alamy, *b* Travelshots.com/Alamy; **p.119** *t* Leslie Garland Picture Library/Alamy, *b* © ullsteinbild/TopFoto; **p.123** Marc Hill/Alamy; **p.125** mediacolor's/ Alamy; **p.126** Robert Brook/Alamy; **p.129** Paul Glendell/Alamy; **p.130** Simon Ross; **p.132** *l* Realimage/Alamy, *r* Mark Boulton/Alamy; **p.133** Rex Features; **p.134** Paul Brown/Rex Features.

**Text and image acknowledgements:**
**p.13** Polly Mitchell: 'My Favourite Place', from *Teaching Geography* (Geographical Association, January, 2003); **p.22** *l* Octopus Publishing Group: *Philip's Atlas of the World*, © 2007 Philip's; *r* © E.H. Shepard and Egmont UK Ltd., reproduced by permission of Curtis Brown Group Ltd., London; **p.47** Helicon Publishing: Talbes: Climate weather data for York and Plymouth, from *World Weather Book*, 5th Revised Edition (Hutchinson, 2000); **p.68** Field Studies Council: Diagram of Pebble Shape Analysis, Power's Index; **p.74** Controller of OPSI: UK Population statistics (2007) from Office for National Statistics, www.statistics.gov.uk, © Crown copyright; **p.75** BBC History Online: Table: UK Population (A.D. 43 - 2005), from http://news.bbc.co.uk/1/hi/uk/4218740.htm; **p.82** A story of immigration © Jerry Adesanmi; **p.90** Bensons Mapguides: Map extract of London (Bensons Mapguides, 2006), © F. Benito and P. Benito; **p.121** Reproduced with kind permission of VisitBlackpool, www.visitblackpool.com; **p.126** CartoonStock: Fly-tipping cartoon, www.cartoonstock.com/directory/f/fly_tipping.asp; **p.131** Recycle.More: Figure 9: Reusing household items, www.recycle-more.co.uk; **p.24, p.41** *t*, **p.57** *b*, **p.61, p.65, p.88, p.93, p.100, p.117** The Controller of her Majesty's Stationery Office: Mapping extracts from Ordnance Survey, © Crown copyright.

Every effort has been made to trace all copyright holders, but if any have been inadvertently overlooked, the Publishers will be pleased to make the necessary arrangements at the first opportunity.

# Introduction

**In this chapter you will study:**

- what the word 'geography' means and what geographers do
- how to be a geographical detective
- how to study issues in Geography
- the geography of exploration
- an introduction to the geography of the UK
- what makes the UK special.

# What is geography?

**Geography** is the study of the world around us. Geographers are interested in the processes and features of the natural world and the ways that people interact, both with each other and with the world around them.

Geography is a very important subject to study at school. It helps us to understand and appreciate the world in which we live. Look at Figure 1. This photograph was taken from the Apollo 17 spacecraft in 1972. If you look at it you can see the continents, the oceans and the clouds. This photograph made many people aware of just how fragile the Earth is, and how important it is that we take care of its natural systems.

## Activity

1 Study the photograph in Figure 1.

a) Why do you think this photograph has such a huge impact on people?

b) How does the photograph make you feel?

c) Can you recognise any features on the Earth (for example, oceans, land masses)? Use an atlas to help you.

▲ **Figure 1  Apollo 17 photo of the Earth (1972)**

## Being a geography detective

Geographers are rather like detectives. They are inquisitive and curious. They like to find out what is happening and why. To be a good geographer, we need to be able to ask searching questions about the world around us.

Look at Figure 2, which is a photograph taken in the Lake District in northwest England. If you look closely at the photograph it raises several interesting geographical questions about the landscape. We could do the same thing for an entirely different landscape, such as a seaside resort in Dorset in the summer (Figure 3).

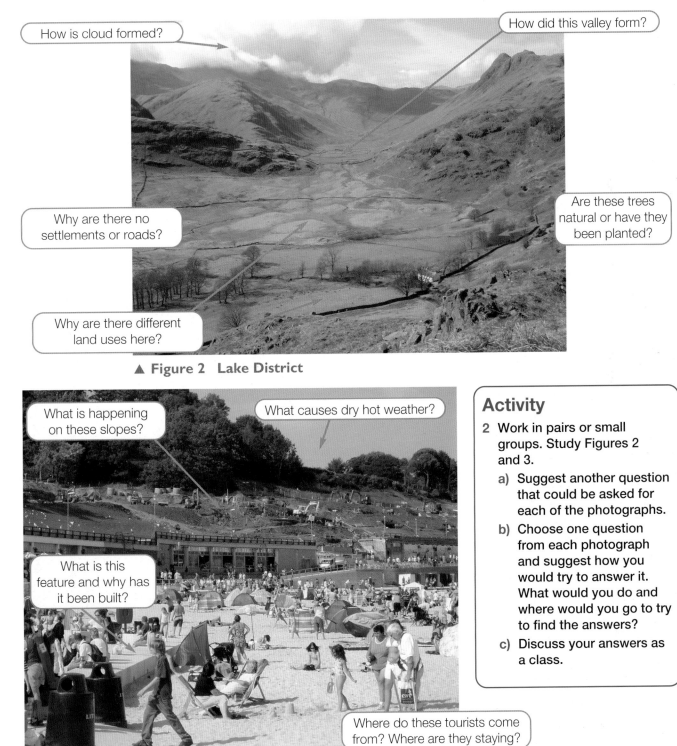

▲ **Figure 2  Lake District**

▲ **Figure 3  Lyme Regis**

## Activity

2 Work in pairs or small groups. Study Figures 2 and 3.

  a) Suggest another question that could be asked for each of the photographs.

  b) Choose one question from each photograph and suggest how you would try to answer it. What would you do and where would you go to try to find the answers?

  c) Discuss your answers as a class.

3

Once we have our geographical questions, we can set about trying to answer them and therefore understand more about what is going on. Look at Figure 4. It outlines the stages of the geographical enquiry process. It is very important to follow these stages in order to make sure that the answers to our geographical questions are accurate and reliable. In this book you will have the opportunity to carry out a number of your own enquiries.

## Activity

3 Work in pairs or small groups. Study the photograph in Figure 5.
   a) Suggest some questions raised by this photograph.
   b) Select one question and suggest how you would try to answer it.

## ICT ACTIVITY

Select a photograph of your choice that shows a recent geographical event, such as a flood or an earthquake. Copy and paste it into a Word document. Use the Draw program to add labels to identify questions that could be asked. You could take this activity a stage further by selecting and trying to answer one of the questions.

**Identification of a question**
What are the effects of tourism in a seaside town?

**Plan the enquiry**
I need to plan when to visit the town to gather information. I need to decide where to go in the town, what to look for and who to speak to. I need to take a camera.

**Collect data**
I need to do a questionnaire to ask peoples' views on tourism. I need to speak to shopkeepers. I need to research newspaper articles.

**Data presentation**
I need to make sense of my data by drawing graphs and diagrams. I may need to work out averages. I may need to draw maps.

**Data analysis**
I now need to interpret and make sense of all my findings. I need to try to find evidence to help me answer the question.

**Conclusion**
This is where I give an answer to my question. How might I improve my study in the future? What are the outcomes of my study?

▲ **Figure 4   Stages of enquiry**

▲ **Figure 5   Typical urban scene**

## Geography in action: the UK floods of 2007

Look at Figure 6. Many parts of the UK suffered from heavy rainfall during the summer of 2007. This led to widespread flooding of towns, roads and railways and farmers' fields. This is a good example of Geography in action.

Geographers are well placed to understand and interpret topical events and issues such as flooding. This is because in Geography we study topics like weather and climate, rivers, urban development, transport and farming. Geographers know, for example, that building houses on floodplains (land where rivers flood) is not a good idea. Geographers know that land close to rivers should be best left as pasture or green spaces for leisure and recreation.

Geographers are good decision makers because they can weigh up arguments and examine options from different viewpoints. They understand the workings of natural and human environments and how they interact. You will have lots of opportunities to make decisions about geographical issues in each chapter of this book.

### Activities

4 Create a notice board in your classroom with the heading 'Geography in Action'. As a class collect recent newspaper articles or articles from the internet (such as from the BBC website at **www.bbc.co.uk/news**) about global issues such as global warming, pollution and natural disasters. Post them on your notice board. Keep refreshing the notice board to keep it up-to-date.

5 Select a recent issue from the news that interests you. Discuss in your class why geographers are well placed to understand and interpret this.

Farmland under water

Normal course of the river with the trees marking the riverbanks

Village of Upton upon Severn cut off by the floods

▲ **Figure 6  Gloucestershire floods in UK, 2007**

# Exploring geography in a changing world

▲ Figure 7   Portrait of James Cook

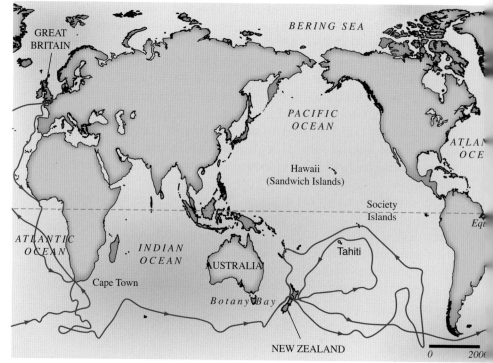

▲ Figure 8   Map of James Cook's second voyage

Can you name any famous explorers? Early explorers and travellers were the original geographers (Figures 7 and 8). They wanted to find out about the Earth. They travelled far and wide taking detailed notes of all that they saw and experienced, and many died in their quests. They were inquisitive and curious, just as people are today.

## Activity

6  Study Figure 8.

a) In which direction did James Cook set out from the UK and through which ocean did he sail?

b) Why do you think he stopped off in Cape Town?

c) Which country did he travel to after leaving Cape Town?

d) Why do you think James Cook's route had so many twists and turns?

e) Would you have liked being on James Cook's Second Voyage? Explain your answer.

## ICT ACTIVITY

Use the internet to find out more about the life and voyages of one of the world's great European explorers, such as James Cook. To get you started access the **http://www.cdli.ca/CITE/explorer.htm** website to find a list of early European explorers.

There are many other websites with interesting information about explorers such as: **http://www.kidinfo.com/American_History/Explorers.html**
A Google search will reveal other useful sites.

Include in your study some facts and figures about your chosen explorer together with maps of the areas explored or discovered.

Although there are fewer new places to discover there are still plenty of places to explore. All places are new to us as individuals until we have explored them. Places and environments are constantly changing and it is often interesting to re-visit places to see how they have changed. You will have the opportunity to visit all sorts of places while you are at school. Make the most of these opportunities!

## Activity

7 Study Figure 9.

a) Choose one of the global issues and suggest why you think it is important.

b) Can you think of any other global issues that are in the news at the moment?

c) Why do you think it is important to study Geography at school?

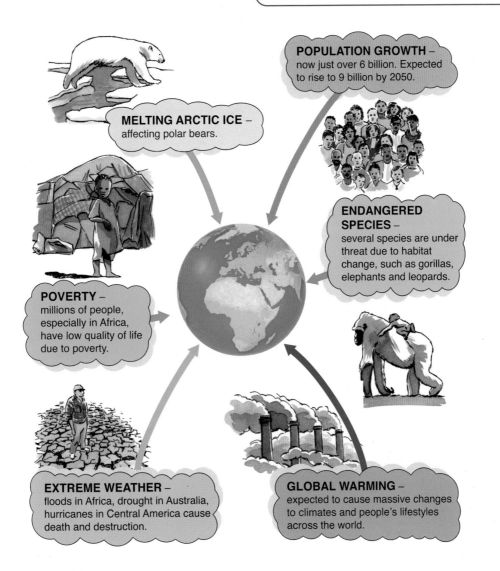

**MELTING ARCTIC ICE** – affecting polar bears.

**POPULATION GROWTH** – now just over 6 billion. Expected to rise to 9 billion by 2050.

**ENDANGERED SPECIES** – several species are under threat due to habitat change, such as gorillas, elephants and leopards.

**POVERTY** – millions of people, especially in Africa, have low quality of life due to poverty.

**EXTREME WEATHER** – floods in Africa, drought in Australia, hurricanes in Central America cause death and destruction.

**GLOBAL WARMING** – expected to cause massive changes to climates and people's lifestyles across the world.

▲ **Figure 9 Current global issues**

The world has changed a great deal since the time of James Cook. Today we face many global issues, as Figure 9 shows. Geographers are well placed to address these issues with their understanding of the human and physical world, and so try to make the world a better place in which to live.

# The geography of the UK

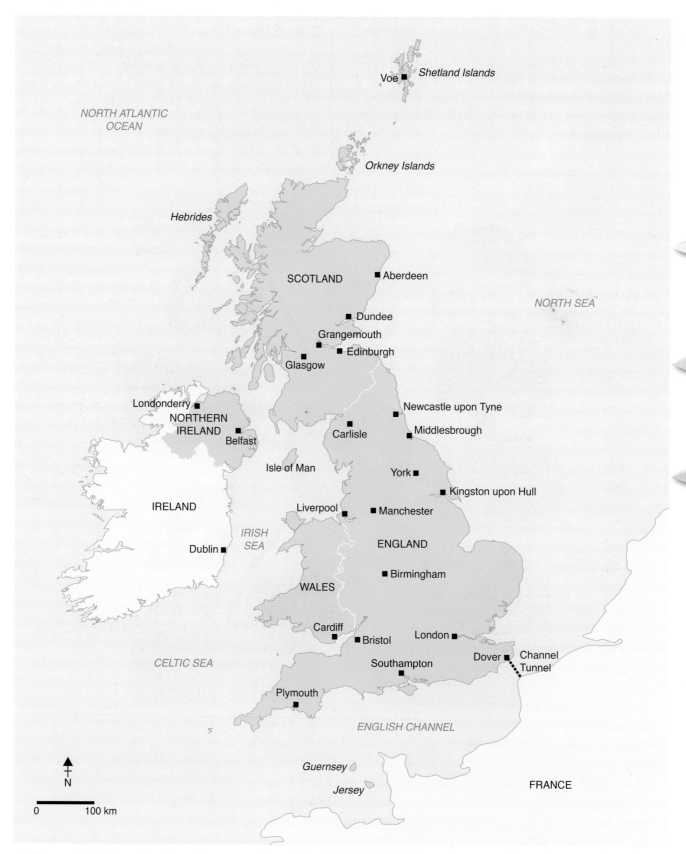

▲ **Figure 10  Map showing the countries of the UK, British Isles and Great Britain**

This book is all about the United Kingdom. Before we start, it is important to understand exactly what the UK is and how it differs from Great Britain and the British Isles. Look at the coloured boxes below.

The UK government is based in London. Regional governments (which have some power over issues such as health, education and transport) operate in Wales, Scotland and Northern Ireland. In Wales, the National Assembly for Wales is based in Cardiff; in Scotland, the Scottish Parliament is in Edinburgh; and in Northern Ireland, the Northern Ireland Assembly operates from Belfast. Within the UK, counties and districts organise the supply of local services (such as waste collection and transport).

- The United Kingdom is made up of the countries of England, Wales, Scotland and Northern Ireland.

- The British Isles includes Ireland (or Eire). Ireland is a separate foreign country (just as France is).

- The term Great Britain (or Britain for short) is used to describe England, Wales and Scotland only.

## Activity

8 Study Figure 10.
   a) Which country is part of the UK, but not part of Great Britain?
   b) Which country is part of the British Isles, but not part of the UK?
   c) Name a city on Figure 10 that is in the British Isles, but is not in the UK.
   d) Which city is the odd one out and why?
      1 London, Birmingham, Cardiff and Bristol
      2 Edinburgh, Dublin, Middlesbrough and Liverpool
      3 Belfast, Manchester, Aberdeen and Cardiff
   e) Where is the Isle of Man? Is it part of the UK?
   f) Name and locate one other island or group of islands that are part of the UK.
   g) Which two countries does the Channel Tunnel link?

## ICT ACTIVITY

Find out a bit more about the workings of the regional parliaments using the following website addresses. What are the issues that the regional parliaments are responsible for?

Wales http://www.wales.gov.uk

Scotland http://www.scottish.parliament.uk/home.htm

Northern Ireland http://www.niassembly.gov.uk

Do you think it is a good idea for regional parliaments to exist in Wales, Scotland and Northern Ireland? Explain your answer. Use the following web link to help you: http://geography.about.com/library/cia/blcuk.htm

## What makes the UK special?

When you return to the UK from a holiday abroad, it is easier than usual to suggest what makes the UK special (Figure 11). When asked, many people have commented on the lush green countryside, fish and chips, driving on the left, red pillar boxes, Marmite, the BBC, and, of course, the English language. The UK has its cathedrals, its tearooms and its pubs. It has its village greens, country houses and cottage gardens. If you visit London or travel from an airport you will have seen shops selling 'British' souvenirs such as miniature London buses and taxis (Figure 12).

There are other things too that make the UK special. We are a multicultural country with people from all over the world choosing to live here. We are a tolerant and fair society, known throughout the world for our laws and system of justice. We are still regarded as an important world power and take an active part in many international discussions.

▲ **Figure 11    Aspects of 'Britishness'**

The UK is one of the most densely populated countries in the world, with over 60 million people. It is one of the richest countries in the world too, with most people enjoying a high **standard of living** and a long life expectancy. We have a varied landscape and a moderate climate with few extremes. For most people, the UK is a pleasant place to live.

However, there are also some negative aspects. These include binge drinking, street violence and litter. Can you think of any others?

10

---

### Activity

9  Work in pairs to design an illustrated mind map or poster with the heading 'What makes the UK special?' Start by brainstorming ideas to create a list of what you consider to be features that make the UK special. Consider the following headings to get you started:

- food
- places
- landscapes
- people
- entertainment
- sport
- music.

Add to your list by looking at one or two websites to discover some facts and figures about the UK (see below). Try to collect some stickers, labels and photos to illustrate your mind map or poster.

**Facts and figures about the UK:**

**http://geography.about.com/library/cia/blcuk.htm**

**National Statistics website:**

**http://www.statistics.gov.uk**

▲ **Figure 12    Souvenir shop**

# My Home Environment

**In this chapter you will study:**

- how to investigate your local environment
- how to draw a mental map
- how to investigate your local heritage
- how to carry out fieldwork in your home environment
- how to investigate hedgerow ecosystems.

# A  Investigating my home environment

Your home environment is a familiar place – the area that you call 'home'. For most of us it is where we live: our home, our garden and the area nearby. There may be other areas that we think of as our 'second homes' because we spend a lot of time there and know these areas well. You probably have several places that can be thought of as home environments (see Figure 1).

When we know a place or an area well, we tend to feel comfortable and safe there. We know our way around and feel confident there. We are also more likely to care for the area and want to look after it. Understanding and caring for environments, however big or small, is at the heart of Geography.

## Activity

1  Prepare some information about your home environment. You could produce a collage of writing and photographs, making use of sketches and drawings. You may choose to include a poem or make a PowerPoint presentation. Decide what makes your home environment special and make sure you include these points in your work.

This is where I live. It is a cottage in the country surrounded by fields. We have a big garden where I like to play football.

I am a Southampton fan and St Mary's Stadium is another place I know well. I like the familiar walk to the stadium and I can find my way around inside the ground. It's a very special place.

I often visit my aunt and uncle who live in Watford. I like to visit the shops and go to see Watford play football.

▲ Figure I   James' home environment

# B Mental maps and favourite places

Look at Figure 2. It is a map drawn by a Year 7 boy of his house and garden. This type of map is called a mental map because it is drawn from memory. Mental maps do not have to be accurate. They just show what is important to the person who is drawing them. They do not have to show everything that is there, for example they could show a whole house or just one room in a house.

The boy who drew the mental map in Figure 2 seems to like the gardens. Notice that he has included a lot of detail about the bushes and trees. However, he hasn't shown much interest in the house, but he knows where the kitchen is!

## Activities

2 Draw a mental map of your home environment. Draw it carefully, so you can produce a good quality map. You can include as many details as you like. Add colours to make your map look attractive.

3 Look at the mental map that you drew for Activity 2.
   a) Identify a feature on your mental map that you particularly like. Describe what makes it so special to you.
   b) How could the home environment that you drew in your mental map be improved?

4 Look at Figure 3. It is a short account written by a Year 7 girl describing her favourite place. Describe your favourite place. You could write an account or a poem. Use drawings if you wish or a photograph with labels. Try to express what makes this place so special to you.

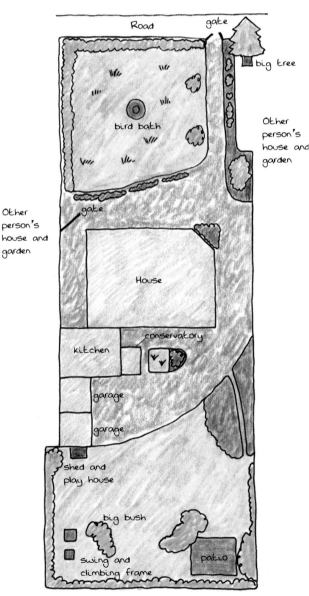

▲ **Figure 2   A mental map**

## My favourite place

My favourite place is probably at my Granny and Grandad's house. I like to sit in the fields and look at the valley and I like to watch the cows and look at the river. The river is tidal. My other favourite place is the beach. It stretches all the way from Appledore to Instow. The beach nearest Appledore is called 'Westward Ho!' and the rest is called 'The Burrows'. There is a pebble ridge and there are rock pools at both ends of the beach. I watched the eclipse on the beach. There are never very many people on 'The Burrows', everyone is usually on Westward Ho. When I watched the eclipse we sat on the ridge and watched the eclipse in pools of salt water on the beach. In the summer it's packed and you can't move for people. But in the winter you can take your dog for a walk on the beach. Clyde loves the beach (Clyde the dog).

▲ **Figure 3   My favourite place**

## C   Investigating our local heritage

In the United Kingdom we are surrounded by many historical features of our **heritage** (Figure 4). These give us an important link with the past and a sense of belonging. Some people like to live in quaint old cottages in the countryside or possess antiques. Old churches, ancient hedgerows and even old red pillar boxes are attractive and interesting historical features in our landscape. Many people who live in recently populated countries (such as Australia or the United States) often say that we are very lucky to have this, as they miss the lack of ancient monuments in their own countries.

> ### Activities
>
> 5 Study Figure 4. Choose one of the examples of heritage that you particularly like.
>   a) Which example have you chosen and why?
>   b) Imagine that this feature was to be removed and replaced with something more modern. How would you feel about this proposal?
> 6 Choose a heritage feature in or close to your home environment. It could be an old building, an ancient hedgerow or tree, a village green or pond, or an old sign or notice.
>   a) Describe the feature in as much detail as you can. Include a photograph or sketch if possible.
>   b) What makes the feature an important part of the local environment?

▲ **Figure 4   Examples of heritage in the local environment**

# LOCAL FIELDWORK

**The following fieldwork exercises will help you investigate your local environment and get a real 'feel' for its character.**

## 1   Post a photo

Take a digital photograph of your local environment. Print the photograph and use it to build up a classroom display of local environments. Add some labels or write a short description of your photograph.

## 2   Write a Haiku poem

A Haiku poem is a short poem that has only three lines. The first line has five syllables, the second line has seven syllables and the third line has five syllables. Look at Figure 5, which is a photograph of a range of hills in Shropshire called the Stiperstones. The following poem is a Haiku poem written by a pupil who had visited the Stiperstones on a fieldtrip.

Rocky and peaceful
The candy-floss blue white sky
Dreamy atmosphere

Count the syllables in each line to see that there are five, seven and five syllables in each.

To write a Haiku poem you need to:

- Find an area of personal space away from other people.

- Look around you, listen and smell.

- Write down some descriptive words (adjectives) about your local environment.

- Use the words to help you write your poem. Remember to follow the syllable rules!

## 3   Be a local environment detective

This activity should be done outside in the local environment. Figure 6 contains a number of stimulus questions intended to help you observe and record the characteristics of your local environment. The questions can be split up within your class and the answers can then be discussed after the exercise has been completed.

▲ **Figure 5   Stiperstones, Shropshire**

- What feature would you like to remove or change and why?

- Suggest one way that people have made this landscape better.

- Would you like to be in this place at night? Explain your answer.

- If you were to come here in six months' time how do you think it would be different?

- Suggest one way that people have made this landscape worse.

- What do you think is the oldest part of this landscape?

- What are the main colours of the landscape?

- Which is your favourite plant or tree and why?

- What sources of pollution can you identify in this landscape?

- What do you think is the newest part of this landscape?

- If you were to take one photograph to show what this place is like, which way would you face and why?

- Which building is your favourite and why?

▲ **Figure 6   Stimulus questions**

## D   The hedgerow ecosystem

Hedges are very common features of the UK landscape. Typically they border fields or roads but they are also very common in towns and cities. Most hedges in urban gardens consist of only a very few types of plant and as a result they do not support many animals. In the countryside, however, hedges are very different and often contain many species of plant and even fully grown trees! They are home to a great number and variety of animals, birds and insects.

Look at Figure 7. It shows a typical British hedgerow beside a country lane in rural Somerset. It is mid-Autumn. Notice that there are lots of wild red hawthorn berries in the hedge. They will help to feed birds during the cold winter days ahead.

*honey-suckle, more like!*

Birds can easily be spotted flitting through the tops of a hedge, but there are many other animals that live in a hedge and these can be much more difficult to see. They may live in the dark depths of the hedge or even in burrows beneath it. They could be very small or perhaps only come out at night.

▲ **Figure 7   Somerset hedgerow in the autumn**

---

### Activities

7   Study Figure 8.
   a)   What do voles eat?
   b)   If you were a woodlouse, what creatures would you do your best to avoid?
   c)   Do sparrowhawks only eat birds?
   d)   Name two 'plant-feeding' insects eaten by insect-eating birds.
   e)   What do owls, sparrowhawks and weasels all have in common?
   f)   If there were no wild flowers in the hedgerow one year, what effect would this have on the food web?

8   Make a copy of the two food chains in Figure 9 and fill in the blank boxes using Figure 8 to help you. You can use words or diagrams.

Look at Figure 8. It is a diagram called a **food web**. It shows how the living organisms in a typical hedgerow are all linked together providing food for one another. The arrows point towards the predators. Notice in Figure 8 that the red berries shown in Figure 7 not only provide food for birds, but are also eaten by voles and mice. These animals in turn provide a tasty meal for birds of prey and weasels. The links from one source of food to another (for example, berry to vole to weasel) is called a **food chain**.

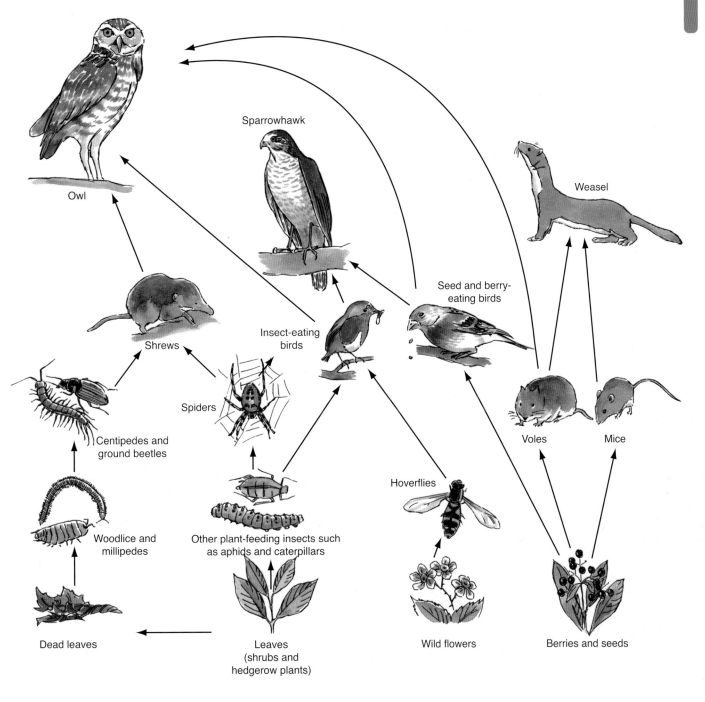

▲ Figure 8   Hedgerow food web

A

| | → | aphid | → | | → | shrew | → | |

B

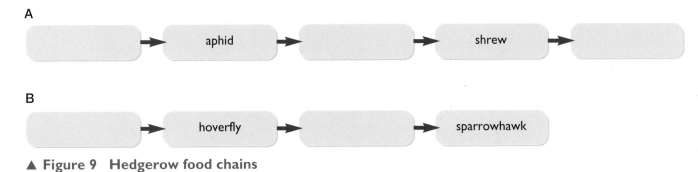

| | → | hoverfly | → | | → | sparrowhawk |

▲ Figure 9   Hedgerow food chains

All the living things in a hedgerow interact with one another and with the environment. This is called an **ecosystem**. Look at Figure 10, which shows a typical hedgerow ecosystem. Notice that the plants, trees and the birds are influenced by environmental factors such as the climate and the soil.

A hedge is an example of a small-scale ecosystem as it only covers a small area. Can you think of any other small-scale ecosystems? It is possible to identify much larger scale ecosystems including deserts, coral reefs and tropical rainforests. Can you think of any others?

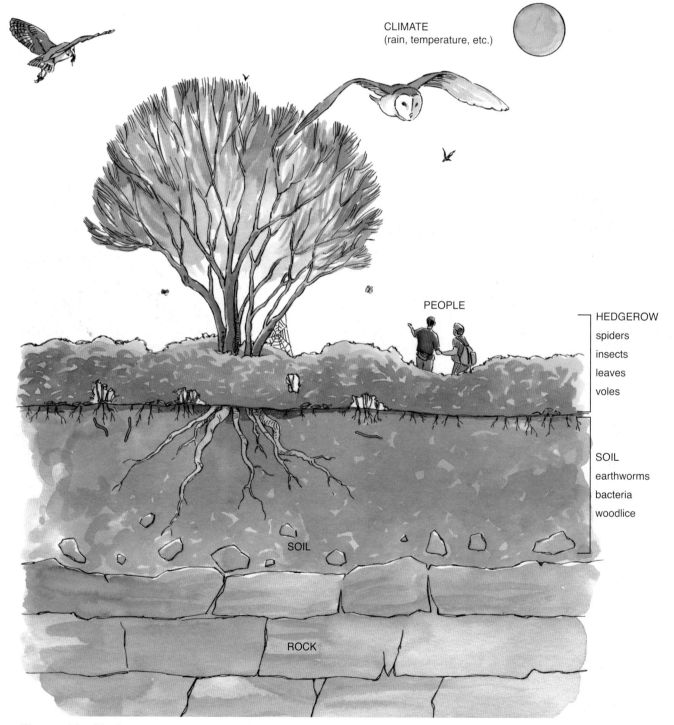

CLIMATE
(rain, temperature, etc.)

PEOPLE

HEDGEROW
spiders
insects
leaves
voles

SOIL
earthworms
bacteria
woodlice

SOIL

ROCK

▲ **Figure 10  Hedgerow ecosystem**

# E   Issue: Should hedgerows be destroyed?

As you have seen in Figure 8, a great variety of living organisms live and depend on hedges. For them, the hedge is a home or **habitat**. If it is destroyed by fire or dug up by people, a large number of individual creatures will lose their home. Hedges also act as **wildlife corridors**, enabling animals to move across the countryside without having to be exposed to possible predators.

It may seem that hedges in the countryside are wild and that they have grown up naturally. They are, however, made by people. Most hedges in the UK were planted during the eighteenth century, although some are far older. They were planted to create separate fields for farming.

Over the years, the number of plant species in a hedgerow increases and fully-grown trees (such as oak and ash) may develop. It is possible to estimate the age of a hedge by counting the number of species of tree and shrub in a 27 m stretch. Each species represents 100 years!

In the 1970s and 1980s, many hundreds of kilometres of hedgerow were uprooted to create larger fields for farming (see Figure 11). Many people are concerned about the loss of hedges and the impact that this has had on the countryside. Today landowners are not only encouraged to keep hedges, but can obtain grants to help them plant and look after hedges.

▲ **Figure 11   Hedgerow destruction**

## Activity

9  Study Figure 11.
   a) What evidence is there on the photograph that a hedgerow has been removed?
   b) What has the landowner done to replace the hedgerow and mark the field boundary?
   c) Why do you think the landowner has used this type of field boundary?
   d) Describe the likely effects of the hedgerow removal on the small stream.
   e) What effect will the removal of the hedgerow have on wildlife?
   f) Do you think the hedgerow should have been removed? Explain your answer.

1 Hedges cast shadows on the edge of fields reducing the growth of crops.

2 Hedges act as wildlife 'corridors'.

3 Hedges mark the edges of fields and help act as boundaries.

4 Hedges need regular cutting and this is expensive.

5 Hedges are attractive and are a natural part of the landscape.

6 Hedges prevent soil erosion by acting as wind breaks.

7 Hedges provide homes and food for wildlife.

8 Hedges take up space that could be used for growing crops.

9 Hedges can harbour weeds and pests.

10 Some hedgerow birds are a nuisance to farmers as they eat the seeds and fruit of crops.

▲ Figure 12   Statements for and against hedgerows

## Activity

10   Study Figure 12. It contains a number of short statements about hedgerows. They are labelled 1 to 10.

   a) Draw up a table with the headings 'statements in favour of hedgerows' and 'statements against hedgerows'. Sort the ten statements in Figure 12 under the two headings.

   b) Use a colour to highlight the most important statement in each column. Explain your choices.

   c) Do you think landowners should be encouraged to plant hedges? Why?

   d) Create a class 'hedge' as a wall display. Include viewpoints from the class about the importance of hedges. Use pictures and material to depict branches and leaves and the organisms likely to be found in the hedge. Use your imagination to make it as realistic and interesting as you can.

## LOCAL FIELDWORK

1   Conduct a field study of a hedgerow in your local area. This could be within your school grounds, close to your home or elsewhere. Attempt some of these activities:

- Take a digital photograph of the hedge and add some labels to describe its main features.

- Plot the hedge on a plan or map of your local area.

- Measure the dimensions of the hedge (height and thickness).

- Try to identify some of the plants in the hedge.

- Is there any evidence of wildlife (e.g. small holes or burrows, insects on leaves or plant stems, birds)?

- Does the hedge have a positive impact on the local environment (e.g. attractive to look at, pleasant smells, interesting sounds, colourful, etc.)?

- Does the hedge have a negative impact on the adjacent land (e.g. shade, height of grass growth)?

2   Having conducted your study, write a summary suggesting whether you think the hedge should be kept, or whether you think it should be cut down. You might like to present your summary in the form of a poem.

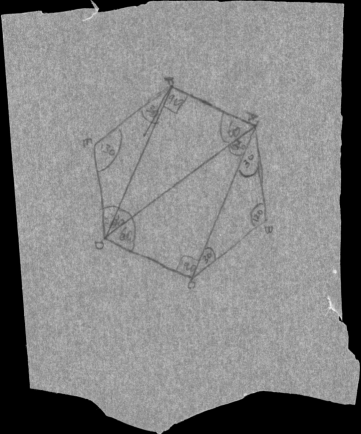

# Ordnance Survey Map Skills

**In this chapter you will study:**

- the differences between plans and maps
- fantasy maps
- Ordnance Survey (OS) mapping
- mapwork skills using 1:50,000 and 1:25,000 maps
- how to interpret OS maps.

# A   What is a map?

A map is a drawing that shows a bird's eye view of an area. It shows where landscape features are in relation to each other. A typical map may contain information about roads, buildings, woodlands and rivers.

Maps come in all sorts of shapes and sizes. Look at Figure 1 to see different types of map. Maps that show relatively small areas (such as the layout of shops in a shopping mall) are called plans. There is probably a plan map for your school.

A good and accurate map must have a **scale**. This shows how distance on the map (in cm or mm) relates to real-life distance on the ground.

On a map, scale is shown in two ways (see Figure 2).

Most maps cover large areas, often many kilometres. They can be obtained as single sheets or as collections in atlases. Increasingly maps can be accessed using the internet and in-car satellite navigation systems.

In a traditional atlas you will find a great range of maps. Some will show the basic geography of countries (e.g. towns, rivers, main roads) and others will show information about climate, vegetation and industrial activity. A road atlas contains detailed information about the road network of an area. It is used to find the best route between places.

## Activities

1 Study the two maps in Figure 3. They were taken from adverts in a local newspaper. Work in pairs to discuss the following questions before writing your answers in your book.

   a) Which of the two maps do you think is the most useful in helping people to find their way to the stores? Explain your answer.

   b) Suggest ways to improve the least useful map.

2 Try to find some advertising maps in your local newspaper. Select one that you consider to be good and one that you think is poor. Stick them in your book and add a few labels giving reasons for your choice.

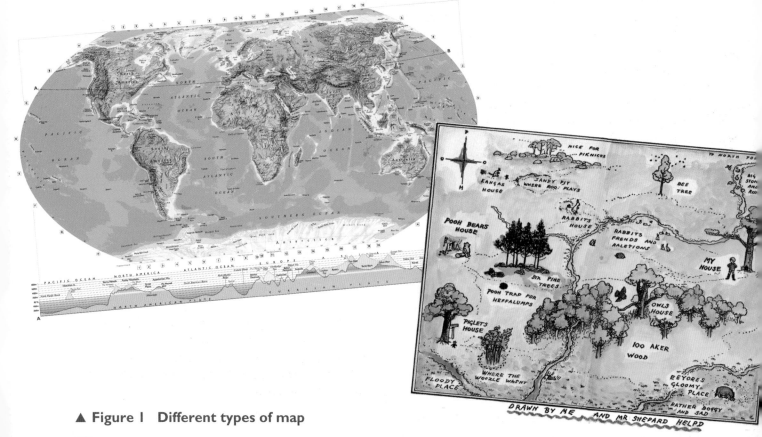

▲ **Figure 1   Different types of map**

(a) Furniture City Ltd

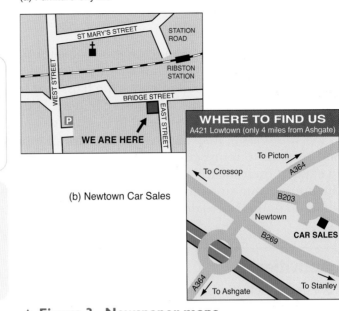

(b) Newtown Car Sales

## 1. Linear scale

Using the scale below, each 2 cm on the map is 1 km on the ground.

km

## 2. Ratio scale

e.g. 1:50,000
This means that one unit on the map equals 50,000 units on the ground. For example: 1 cm on the map equals 50,000 cm ($\frac{1}{2}$ km) on the ground (or 2 cm = 1 km, as shown on the linear scale above).

▲ **Figure 2    Use of scale on maps**

▲ **Figure 3    Newspaper maps**

## B    Fantasy maps

Fantasy maps are maps of the imagination. Most of you will be familiar with the *Winnie the Pooh* stories set within the 'Hundred Acre Wood' (Figure 1). The purpose of the map is to create a landscape and an environment where the stories take place. The map helps us to imagine the scene set by the author A.A. Milne. It shows some of the main features that appear in the books and helps us to understand their relative location.

Fantasy maps can be drawn for small areas, such as 'Hundred Acre Wood', or for much larger areas, such as 'Middle Earth' in the *Lord of the Rings* books. Can you think of any other examples of fantasy maps used in literature?

## Activities

3   Draw a fantasy map for a volcanic island, using the following information to help you. Use colours to make the map attractive. Make up your own names for major landscape features (such as bays, mountain peaks and caves).

- The island is roughly pear-shaped and it is about 15 km in length at its maximum extent.
- The coastline has many headlands and bays of different shapes and sizes. The headlands are rocky and have cliffs and caves. The bays are sandy.
- There are volcanic mountains in the centre of the island.

- There is dense forest around the lower slopes of the mountains and stretching down close to the seashore.
- The tops of the mountains are bare and rocky with few trees.
- Several rivers run down to the sea from the mountains.
- There is one small village close to the sea and next to one of the rivers.

4   Having drawn your fantasy island map now attempt to write a short story based on the map that you have drawn.

## C  OS map skills: using map symbols

OS maps contain an enormous amount of information. Imagine how difficult it would be if all the landscape features shown on the two OS maps of New Galloway (on the flaps that fold out from the front and the back of the book) were in text. The writing would be so small that you would not be able to read it!

For this reason, map makers (called **cartographers**) use colours and **symbols** to represent the different features. A key is then used to explain their meaning. You will soon remember the meaning of the more common symbols, but it is always a good idea to look them up in the key to double-check that you are correct.

### Activities

5  For this Activity you will need to use a set of colouring pencils. Make a copy of the table in Figure 4. Use the keys to the two OS maps (found in the front and the back of the book) to complete the table.

6  Study the 1:50,000 map key in the back of the book. The following short story contains ten references to features explained in the key. Identify each feature using its correct symbol from the key.

> Jeff the cat often liked to explore the quarry near his home in the local village post office. One day, on his way home after a busy night's exploring, he was feeling thirsty and decided to go to the nearby canal for a drink. Feeling refreshed, he strolled along the towpath until he reached the 'Pickled Ferret', a popular waterside public house. From here he scampered through the mixed wood to the picnic site, where he knew there were often scraps of food to be found. Licking his lips, he set off once again for home along the bridleway. He walked past the nature reserve, and the windmill, and then sprang through his familiar cat-flap with a loud 'meow'.

7  Write a similar story including references to ten features from the key of the 1:25,000 OS map in the front of the book. Draw the correct symbol instead of the word in your story.

| 1:50,000 map | | 1:25,000 map | |
|---|---|---|---|
| Symbol | Meaning | Symbol | Meaning |
| | motorway |  (trees) | |
|  - - - - | | | place of worship with a tower |
| | level crossing | 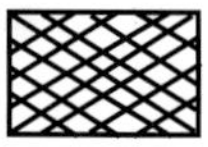 (cross-hatch) | |
| (symbol) | | | picnic site |
| | mixed wood | FB | |
| | post office | | Town Hall |
|  (H) | | | spring |
|  (X) | |  (trees) | |
| | youth hostel |  (marsh symbol) | |
|  (V) | | | walks/trails |

▲ Figure 4   OS symbols

**24**

# D  OS map skills: grid references

To find our way around on an OS map, we make use of the light blue grid lines that run across the maps. Look at the 1:50,000 map at the back of the book. Notice that each blue line has a number written by it. The numbers increase in two directions:

- from left to right across the map (these lines are called eastings)
- from bottom to top across the map (these lines are called northings).

The gridlines make it possible to locate places using grid references.

## How to find a four-figure grid reference

A **four-figure grid reference** is used to identify a particular grid square. The main thing to remember is that each gridline number refers to the next square, either across the map or up the map. To locate a particular grid square, first read along the bottom to find the eastings number. Then read up the side to find the northings number. The two sets of numbers give the **four-figure grid reference**. Look at Figure 5 to see how it works.

Locate New Galloway on the 1:50,000 map at the back of the book. Notice that it is in grid square 6377. Now find St John's Town of Dalry. What is its four-figure grid reference?

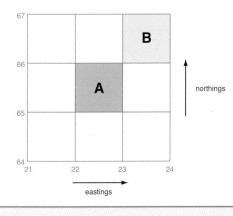

Square **A** has a four-figure grid reference of **2265**.
What is the four-figure grid reference of square **B**?

▲ **Figure 5   How to find a four-figure grid reference**

## Activities

8  Study the 1:50,000 map at the back of the book.
   a) Give the four-figure reference for the village of Balmaclellan.
   b) Which of the following two grid squares would you go to if you wanted to walk in woods: 6076 or 6380?
   c) What is the name of the lake (loch) in grid square 6183?
9  Study the 1:25,000 map at the front of the book.
   a) In what grid square is the flat land called 'Holm of Dalry' located?
   b) What is the name of the lake (loch) in grid square 6381?

## How to find a six-figure grid reference

A **six-figure reference** can locate a place more accurately within a grid square. To give a six-figure grid reference, you have to imagine that the distance between two gridlines is divided into tenths. Whilst it is possible to use a ruler to split a square into tenths, it is good enough to make a careful estimate. (Look at Figure 6 to see how this works.)

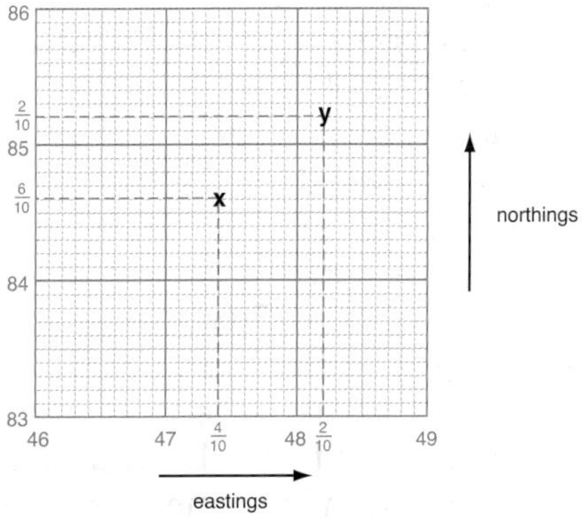

- Starting with the easting, the point **x** lies 47 whole squares and $\frac{4}{10}$ between gridline 47 and gridline 48. This is written **474** and forms the first three figures of the six-figure reference.
- Reading upwards, point **x** lies 84 whole squares and $\frac{6}{10}$ between gridlines and 84 and 85. This is written **846** and forms the second set of figures.
- The complete six-figure grid reference for point **x** is **474846**.

(What is the six-figure grid reference of point **y**?)

▲ **Figure 6   How to find a six-figure grid reference**

# E   OS map skills: compass directions

A **compass** is an instrument often used by people to find direction or to locate themselves accurately (Figure 7). The Earth's magnetic field causes the needle in the compass to rotate as the instrument is moved. The needle points north towards the North Pole and south towards the South Pole.

The points of a compass can also be used in map reading (see Figure 8). North usually points straight up a map, from the bottom to the top. This is always the case with OS maps (south is at the bottom, east to the right and west to the left). Occasionally with some maps this is not the case, so it is important to look in the key to check the direction of north. All maps should have a north point.

The points of a compass are used to give direction. The most important thing about giving a compass direction is to state very clearly which way you are looking or travelling. For example, on the 1:50,000 map at the back of the book, Balmaclellan is to the northeast of New Galloway. New Galloway is to the southwest of Balmaclellan. Where is Balmaclellan in relation to St John's Town of Dalry?

## Activities

10  Study the 1:50,000 map at the back of the book. Are the following statements true or false? Correct any statements that are false.
   a) St John's Town of Dalry is to the northeast of Balmaclellan.
   b) The Water of Ken runs to the east of New Galloway.
   c) The A713 is east of the B7075.
   d) The A702 enters St John's Town of Dalry from an easterly direction.
   e) The B7075 runs roughly east to west.

11  Study the 1:25,000 map at the front of the book. Find Mulloch Hill in grid square 6380. In what direction would you need to walk if you wanted to get to the following places:
   a) St John's Town of Dalry?
   b) The car park at 624801?
   c) Moss Roddock Loch?
   d) New Galloway?
   e) Trolane Bridge at 644811?

▲ Figure 7   Using a compass

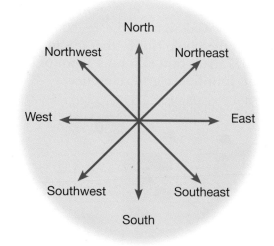

▲ Figure 8   Points of the compass

# F OS map skills: measuring distance

## 1 Straight-line distance

To measure distance, you need to convert the distance between two places on the map (usually in cm) to the real life distance on the ground (usually in km). You have already learned that on an OS map the light blue grid lines are drawn 1 km apart. This means that by simply counting the squares you can get a rough idea of distance on the ground.

To be more accurate you should use a ruler. Measure the distance between the two places and record your answer in centimetres (see Figure 9). Now convert this to kilometres on the ground by placing your ruler alongside the linear scale on the map (see Figure 9). You will soon remember that on a 1:50,000 map, 2 cm equals 1 km and that on a 1:25,000 map, 4 cm equals 1 km.

Look at the 1:50,000 map at the back of the book. Locate the church with a tower in St John's Town of Dalry and the church with a tower in New Galloway. By counting the grid squares between the two churches you can see that the distance is approximately 3 km. Now measure the distance using a ruler. It comes to 6.3 cm. This converts to just over 3 km distance on the ground.

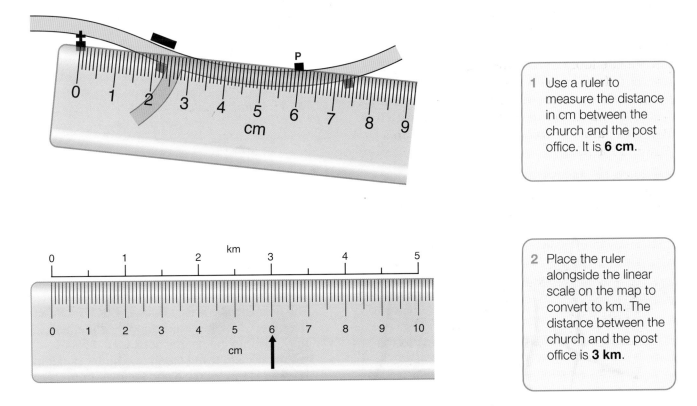

1   Use a ruler to measure the distance in cm between the church and the post office. It is **6 cm**.

2   Place the ruler alongside the linear scale on the map to convert to km. The distance between the church and the post office is **3 km**.

▲ **Figure 9   Measuring straight-line distance**

## 2 Curved distance

Measuring a straight-line distance is relatively simple. However, most of the time movement between places involves travelling along bendy roads or footpaths. We therefore need to be able to measure curved distance as well as straight-line distance.

Measuring curved distances, say along a road or river, is rather more time-consuming and fiddly. The simplest method involves pivoting the straight edge of a piece of paper alongside the curved line (see Figure 10), marking off straight sections on the paper's edge. The total straight-line distance along the edge of the paper can then be converted into kilometres using the linear scale.

Now try to find the curved-line distance along the A713 from Ken Bridge at 641784 to its junction with the A702 in St John's Town of Dalry (see 1:50,000 map at the back of the book. You should find this to be about 8 cm. Now convert this to kilometres.

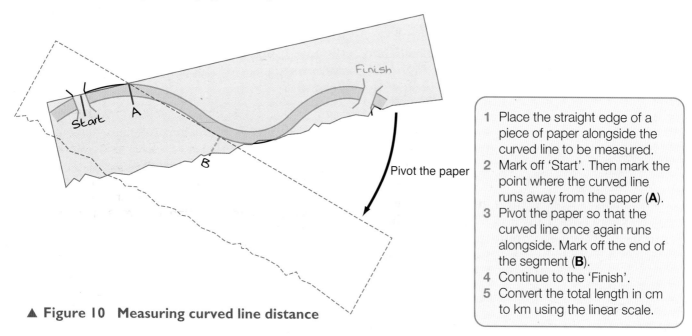

1. Place the straight edge of a piece of paper alongside the curved line to be measured.
2. Mark off 'Start'. Then mark the point where the curved line runs away from the paper (**A**).
3. Pivot the paper so that the curved line once again runs alongside. Mark off the end of the segment (**B**).
4. Continue to the 'Finish'.
5. Convert the total length in cm to km using the linear scale.

▲ **Figure 10   Measuring curved line distance**

# Activities

12  Study the 1:50,000 map at the back of the book. Victor (or Vel as, he was known to his friends) was a crow who liked to perch on the church roof in New Galloway at 632783. One day he decided to visit a few of his friends for tea and biscuits. Find out how far he travelled by measuring the straight-line distances ('as the crow flies!') between the following places. Record your cm reading and the converted km distance.

a) From the church in New Galloway to Kenmure Castle in grid square 6376.

b) From Kenmure Castle to the church (without a tower or spire) in Balmaclellan.

c) From the church in Balmaclellan to the mast on Fintloch Hill in grid square 6178.

d) From the mast on Fintloch Hill back to the church in New Galloway.

e) How far did Vel the crow fly in total?

13  Study the 1:25,000 map at the front of the book. Every year on Boxing Day, the local ducks meet at Coom Bridge (in grid square 6180) for a race down the Water of Ken towards New Galloway. The finishing line is Ken Bridge at 641784. After the race, when they have dried their feathers, they pop into the nearby hotel for a bowl of warm milk and some bread and butter pudding. How far is the course along the river from Coom Bridge to Ken Bridge? Record your cm reading and the converted km distance.

14  You have been asked to plan a route for a sponsored cycle ride using the roads on the 1:50,000 map at the back of the book. The total distance must be between 8 to 12 km. Make up a route for the cycle ride. Either describe your chosen route, referring to place names, road numbers and grid references, or draw a simple sketch map. Record the total distance of your route.

# G  OS map skills: describing relief

The physical landscape of an area is called its **relief**. Ordnance Survey maps show information about the relief of an area by the detailed and accurate plotting of contours. A **contour** is a line that joins points of equal height above sea level. On an OS map, contours are shown as brown lines. On a 1:50,000 map, the contours are drawn at intervals of 10 metres. On a 1:25,000 map, they are drawn at every 5 metres.

Locate grid square 6682 on the 1:50,000 map extract at the back of the book. There are lots of contours in this square. Notice how some of the contour values are written in brown. As the contour interval is known (10 m), the heights of the other contours can be worked out. Notice also that every fifth contour (the 200 m and the 250 m) is bolder and darker than the others. This is also the case on a 1:25,000 map, although the interval between each darker contour is 25 m.

The spacing between contours tells us how steep a slope is (see Figure 11). The closer the contours are together, the steeper the slope. Contour patterns help to inform us about some of the features of the land, as Figure 12 shows.

The height of the land is shown in other ways too. **Spot heights** are small black or brown dots with a number written alongside. The number is the height in metres above sea level. In grid square 6582 there is a 162 m spot height next to the road. What are the two spot heights in grid square 6581?

## Activities

15  Study the 1:50,000 map at the back of the book.

   a) Locate grid square 6176. What is the height of the top of Peal Hill?

   b) What is the height of the dark brown contour that wiggles its way around Fintloch Hill in grid square 6178?

   c) What is the height of the dark brown contours in grid square 6576?

   d) Can you find a grid square that has a 300 m contour?

   e) What is the lowest spot height on the map? Give its six-figure grid reference.

16  Study the 1:25,000 map at the front of the book.

   There has been a heavy fall of snow in the area and you and your family decide to drive from New Galloway to find a good slope for tobogganing. Only the 'A' roads (red) are open. Select using a six-figure grid reference a good place to go tobogganing. Give reasons for your choice.

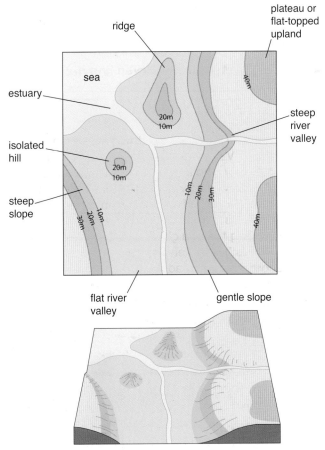

▲ **Figure 12  Contours and landscapes**

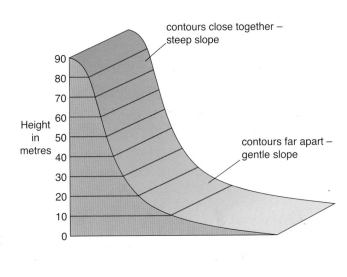

▲ **Figure 11  Contours and slope steepness**

# H   OS map skills: drawing a cross-section

A cross-section is like taking a 'slice' through the landscape. It is more of a sideways view of a landscape (in comparison with a map or a plan, which gives a bird's eye view). Cross-sections help us to see more accurately what the landscape looks like and as such they are very valuable to geographers.

To draw a cross-section, you need to follow the steps below and refer to Figure 13.

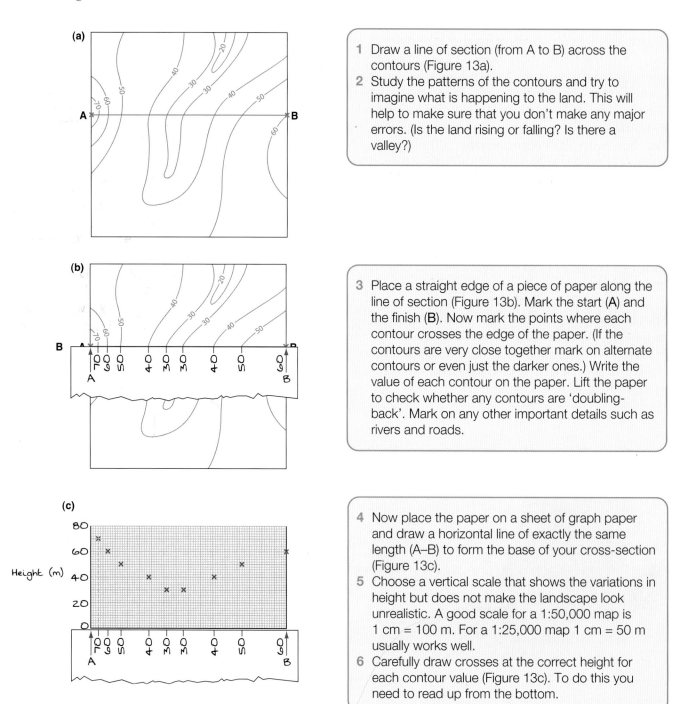

1  Draw a line of section (from A to B) across the contours (Figure 13a).
2  Study the patterns of the contours and try to imagine what is happening to the land. This will help to make sure that you don't make any major errors. (Is the land rising or falling? Is there a valley?)

3  Place a straight edge of a piece of paper along the line of section (Figure 13b). Mark the start (A) and the finish (B). Now mark the points where each contour crosses the edge of the paper. (If the contours are very close together mark on alternate contours or even just the darker ones.) Write the value of each contour on the paper. Lift the paper to check whether any contours are 'doubling-back'. Mark on any other important details such as rivers and roads.

4  Now place the paper on a sheet of graph paper and draw a horizontal line of exactly the same length (A–B) to form the base of your cross-section (Figure 13c).
5  Choose a vertical scale that shows the variations in height but does not make the landscape look unrealistic. A good scale for a 1:50,000 map is 1 cm = 100 m. For a 1:25,000 map 1 cm = 50 m usually works well.
6  Carefully draw crosses at the correct height for each contour value (Figure 13c). To do this you need to read up from the bottom.

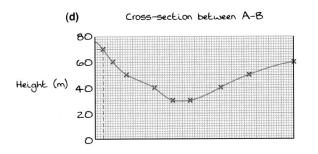

**(d)** Cross-section between A–B

Height (m)

7 Use a freehand curve to join up the crosses (Figure 13d). Continue the curve to both axes. Notice how this has been done at the start of the section, where the value at A lies somewhere between 70 m and 80 m.
8 Complete your section by writing labels and giving your diagram a title (Figure 13d).

▲ **Figure 13 (a, b, c and d)   Drawing a cross-section**

## Activities

17 Draw a cross-section across the valley of the Water of Ken using the 1:25,000 map at the front of the book.
   a) Your cross-section will start at the 171 m spot height on Fintloch Hill (616786) and finish at the 170 m triangulation pillar on the top of Mulloch Hill (631807).
   b) On your sheet of paper mark on the dark brown contours only.
   c) Mark also the two main roads and the river.
   d) Use a copy of the graph axes in Figure 14. Notice that the vertical scale is 1 cm = 50 m.
   e) Complete your cross-section by following the steps outlined above. (Notice that the river valley is quite flat. Don't forget to add labels and a title.)

18 Use the cross-section completed in Activity 17 to answer the following questions. (Notice that the lefthand valley slope is SW of the river whereas the righthand valley slope is to the NE of the river.)
   a) Compare the two valley sides. Are they similar, or is one steeper than the other?
   b) If you were on the A762, would you look down to or up to the A713?
   c) Describe the location of the river (Water of Ken) in its valley bottom.
   d) Why do you think the A713 is not located on the flat land closer to the river?
   e) Why do you think there are very few houses on the NE valley slope leading up to Mulloch Hill?

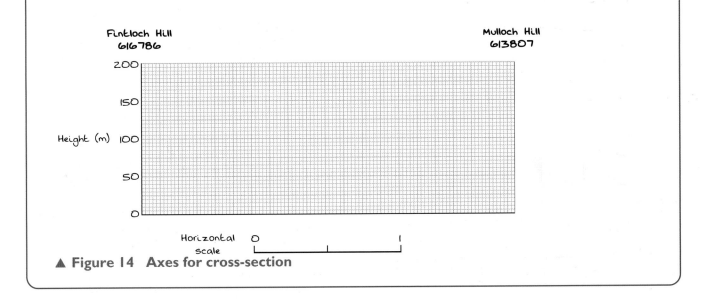

▲ **Figure 14   Axes for cross-section**

# 1 OS map skills: drawing a sketch map

A sketch map is a simple map that shows some (but not all) of the information on an OS map. It is useful in helping to focus on one aspect of the landscape (such as rivers or roads).

When drawing a sketch map, you need to make use of the grid lines on an OS map. They act as guidelines when copying information from the original map. They also help to ensure that your sketch is as accurate as possible. If your guidelines are drawn at exactly the same distance apart as the grid lines on the OS map, then your map will be of the same scale. By increasing or reducing the distance between the guidelines, you can enlarge or reduce the size of your sketch map.

To draw a sketch map, you need to follow the steps shown right and refer to Figure 15.

1. Draw a grid frame matching the area of the map to be sketched. If you are doing the sketch to the same scale as the original then the squares will need to be the same size. You may wish to reduce or enlarge the map by altering the distance between the grid lines.
2. Write the grid numbers at the edge of your frame.
3. Now very carefully transfer the information that you want from the original map to your own using the grid lines to guide you. Figure 15 has been drawn to show the pattern of the main roads in the area more clearly.
4. Complete your sketch by:
   - using colours to make the map clearer
   - adding place names and other labels
   - adding a scale and a north point
   - adding a key
   - writing a title.

## Activities

19  Study the 1:25,000 map extract at the front of the book. Draw a sketch map of the whole area in the map extract to help you investigate the road pattern. Begin by drawing a grid (4 x 5) to exactly the same scale as the map (i.e. 4 cm between each grid line). Now carefully use a pencil to mark on the following information:
- all A and B roads (don't forget to write the number of each road alongside, e.g. A713)
- the Water of Ken river
- the location of New Galloway and St John's Town of Dalry.

Complete your sketch map by:
a) using colours to make the map clearer
b) adding place names and other labels
c) adding a scale and a north point
d) adding a key
e) writing a title.

20  Study the 1:25,000 map extract at the front of the book. The local council have decided to locate a new car park in grid square 6379.
a) Draw an enlarged sketch map to show some of the features that you think are relevant to this issue. Mark on to your sketch map where you think the car park should be located.
b) Complete the sketch map (labels, title, etc.).
c) Write a few sentences giving the reasons for the location of your car park.

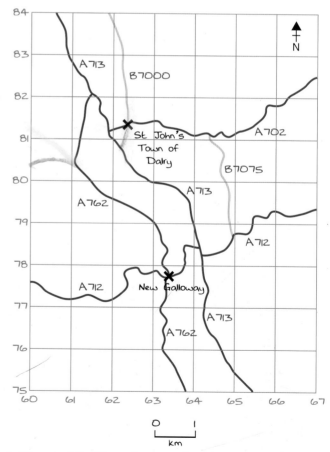

▲ **Figure 15   Sketch map showing the location of New Galloway and St John's Town of Dalry**

# J OS map skills: interpreting photographs

Look at Figure 16. It is a ground photograph of the High Street in New Galloway (taken by the author standing on the ground). If you look closely at the photograph you can find out about the area. To the right is a hotel. On the left, the green painted building houses a tearoom. Can you spot the Post Office sign on the righthand side of the street?

You can use the photograph to pose questions, such as why there are no people in the photograph.

▲ **Figure 16    Ground photo of New Galloway**

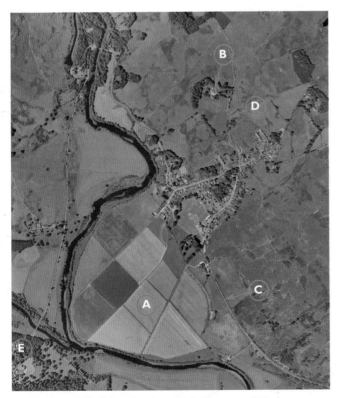

▲ **Figure 17    Vertical aerial photo of Dalry**

Another type of photograph is an aerial photograph (Figure 17). It provides a great deal of information about an area and shows the relative positions of landscape features in much the same way as a map does. Aerial photographs can either show a **vertical view** (Figure 17) or it can be taken at more of an angle to show an oblique view (Figure 18).

To work out which direction a photograph is looking, you need to locate on a map some of the features shown at the bottom, middle and top of the photograph. This gives you a line of sight. You can then locate these features on a map and use the compass directions to help you work out which way the photograph is looking.

Increasingly photographs are being taken from space. Satellite photographs can show an incredible amount of detail. You have probably come across the 'Google Earth' website. They are relatively easy to take and they can be very up-to-date. They are digital photographs and can be altered and enhanced using computer technology in the same way that you can alter digital photos on your home computer.

◀ **Figure 18   Oblique aerial photo of Flamborough**

## Activities

21  Study Figure 16.

   a) Do the buildings appear to be well looked after? Give reasons for your answer.

   b) The High Street has two tearooms. One is the green building on the left and the other is at the far end of the High Street. What does this tell you about one of the functions of New Galloway?

   c) Suggest reasons why there are no people in the photograph.

   d) Do you think the High Street would be interesting to walk along? Explain your answer.

   e) How would you improve the High Street to make it more appealing to you?

22  For this Activity you will need to make use of the aerial photograph (Figure 17) and the 1:25,000 map at the front of the book. An alternative ICT approach using the Multimap.com website is detailed in the ICT Activity. Either way you should answer the following questions:

   a) What is the name of the area of ploughed fields at **A**?

   b) What is the name of the house at **B**?

   c) What is the number of the main road at **C**?

   d) What is the number of the main road at **D**?

   e) What is the name of the river at **E**?

   f) Why is it easy to spot St John's Town of Dalry on the aerial photograph?

   g) Each member of the class should make up an additional question that makes use of both the photograph and the map. These questions can be 'pooled' and used as extra questions to answer in class or as a quiz.

### ICT ACTIVITY

Access the Multimap website at **www.multimap.co.uk**

Type 'St John's Town of Dalry' into the 'placename' search box. Now use the zoom function to find the 1:25,000 map. It should look the same as the map at the front of the book. Now click 'aerial photo'. By moving the mouse around, you should see the map become superimposed over the photograph.

Now attempt the questions in Activity 22.

# Weather and Climate

**In this chapter you will study:**

- definitions of weather and climate
- how to study local climates
- weather in the UK
- how the weather affects us
- the Boscastle flash flood (2004)
- climate of the UK
- climate change in the UK.

# A   What is weather and climate?

Look at the photographs in Figure 1. They show different types of weather experienced in the UK. The word weather is used to describe short-term events such as heavy rainfall, snow or hot sunshine. The **weather** is about what is happening in the atmosphere now or over a period of a few hours or days.

▲ **Figure 1    Weather in the UK**

## Activities

1   Study Figure 1.

   a)   Make a copy of the opinion lines in Figure 2. Consider how the weather in each of the photographs in Figure 1 appeals to you. Place a cross on each of the opinion lines to show your opinion. The further to the right of the line you place the cross, the more you like the weather.

   b)   Show your results to your neighbour and discuss the reasons for your decisions.

   c)   In a few sentences explain your opinion of the weather shown in each of the photographs.

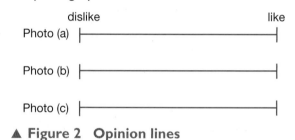

```
              dislike                    like
Photo (a)  ├──────────────────────────┤

Photo (b)  ├──────────────────────────┤

Photo (c)  ├──────────────────────────┤
```

▲ **Figure 2    Opinion lines**

2   Consider the weather that you have experienced today.

   a)   Describe what the weather has been like today.

   b)   Copy the table in Figure 3. Describe how today's weather has affected you by completing the table.

| Description of today's weather | How the weather has affected the clothes I have worn | How the weather has affected what I have had to eat and drink | How the weather has affected what I have done today | How the weather has affected how I have felt today |
|---|---|---|---|---|
|  |  |  |  |  |

▲ **Figure 3    How the weather affects me**

 **ICT ACTIVITY**

Access the BBC Weather Centre at **http://www.bbc.co.uk/weather/**. Click your home region.

• Describe the weather for the day in your home region.

• What is the forecast for the next few days? (You could record the weather to see how accurate this forecast turns out to be!)

• What is the weather elsewhere in the UK?

• If you weren't at home, where in the UK would you like to be and why?

• Is any extreme weather forecast for the UK? If so, what is it and where is it forecast?

When the weather is averaged out over a long period of time, usually 30 years, the word **climate** is used. In the UK we experience a **temperate** climate. This means that we don't suffer from extremes of rainfall or temperature. Other global climates that you may have heard about include **desert**, **tropical** and **arctic**.

In recent years we have all heard a lot about climate change. This is describing long-term changes in temperature and rainfall over a period of many years. Scientists believe that the world is becoming warmer – you have probably heard the term '**global warming**'. There is much concern about the effect this warming might be having on the world's natural environments (Figure 4). We will consider global warming in more detail at the end of this chapter.

▲ **Figure 4**

## Activities

3  Study the photograph in Figure 4.

   a)  Describe what is happening.

   b)  Notice that there is no caption (heading) for the photograph. Write your own caption for the photograph.

   c)  What is the link between this photograph and global warming?

   d)  From your own general knowledge suggest why we should be concerned about global warming.

4  Complete a weather log describing the weather for a week.

   a)  On a copy of the Weather Log (Figure 5) record your observations of the day's weather. You will need to do this at the same time each day if possible.

   b)  At the end of the week represent this information in the form of a diagram like the one in Figure 6.

   c)  Place your diagram in the centre of a larger sheet of paper to create a poster. Illustrate your poster with drawings or photographs of the weather to make it attractive. Don't forget to include a title!

| Date | Time | Temperature (°C) | Wind | Rain / cloud |
|------|------|------------------|------|--------------|
| Tues 3rd Oct | 10.00am | 10° | Breezy | ☁ |
| | | | | |
| | | | | |

Record the temperature using a thermometer in the shade

Record one of the following: Calm (No wind); Gentle; Breezy; Strong; Gale (Very strong wind)

Record using a weather symbol

▲ **Figure 5  Weather observation log**

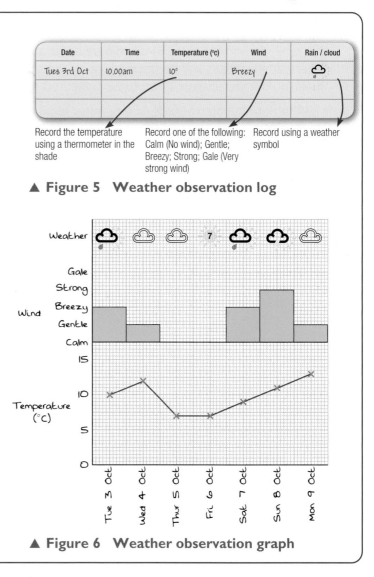

▲ **Figure 6  Weather observation graph**

## LOCAL FIELDWORK

## Studying local climates

**The school environment is an excellent place to study local climatic variations, especially temperature and winds. The best time to look for local variations is usually on a sunny day in spring or autumn fairly early in the morning.**

● Identify a number of safe locations (ideally 20 to 30) around the school to collect the weather information. It is important to choose a good range of locations, including tarmac areas, playing fields, under trees, close to and far away from buildings, and in narrow passageways as well as open areas. Take time to discuss and think carefully about where to conduct your survey. Figure 7 shows some sites chosen for a local climate study at a school in Hertfordshire.

● Split the class into pairs to cover the sites identified. Assume that each pair will be able to collect readings from two sites.

● At each location record the temperature, wind speed and direction. It is really important to try to do this as accurately as possible, as others in your class will be dependent on your results. Why do you think the measurements need to be collected at the same time?

● Make a note in your records of any other local environmental conditions that you think might be important in affecting the measurements you have recorded (e.g. in the shade or next to a hot air vent from the kitchen).

● Present your information in the form of a map (Figure 7). Try to suggest reasons for the patterns you have observed.

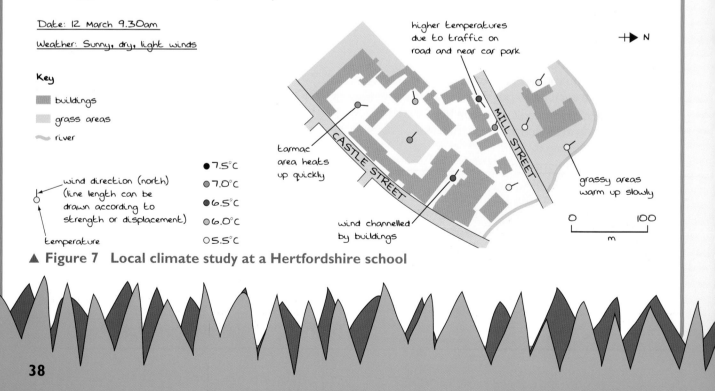

▲ **Figure 7   Local climate study at a Hertfordshire school**

# B Weather in the UK

In the UK our weather is very mixed and changeable. A few sunny dry days will often be followed by wet and windy weather. The reason why our weather varies so much – and why people in the UK are always talking about the weather – is because we are located at a weather roundabout!

Look at Figure 8. Notice that large bodies of air called **air masses** affect the UK. These air masses approach the UK from different directions bringing with them different types of weather. The wind direction that we experience is the main clue to the air mass that is affecting us at any given time. For example, a northerly wind (wind coming from the north) usually means that we are being affected by the cold Arctic air mass.

The UK is rather like a roundabout at the centre of these different airflows. Instead of flows of traffic, the air masses are flows of weather. It is the constantly changing air masses spreading their influence over the UK that explains our changeable weather.

## Activity

5 Read the three air mass descriptions in Figure 9.
   a) Use Figure 8 to help you identify the correct names of the air masses.
   b) What sort of clothing would you need to wear if you were being affected by each of the three air masses in Figure 9?
   c) Write your own air mass description for one other air mass. See if your neighbour can work out which one it is.

**A** I am a cold air mass. I have come from the north and usually visit the UK in the winter. I often bring snow to the north of the UK and bitterly cold winds.

**B** I am a wet and often windy air mass. I have travelled a long way over the Atlantic Ocean. I often bring cloudy but mild weather to the UK.

**C** I am a hot and dry air mass. I visit the UK all the way from North Africa. I am usually very popular in the UK because I bring hot sunny weather in the summer.

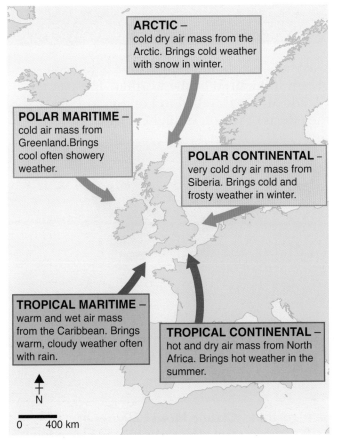

**ARCTIC –** cold dry air mass from the Arctic. Brings cold weather with snow in winter.

**POLAR MARITIME –** cold air mass from Greenland. Brings cool often showery weather.

**POLAR CONTINENTAL –** very cold dry air mass from Siberia. Brings cold and frosty weather in winter.

**TROPICAL MARITIME –** warm and wet air mass from the Caribbean. Brings warm, cloudy weather often with rain.

**TROPICAL CONTINENTAL –** hot and dry air mass from North Africa. Brings hot weather in the summer.

N

0    400 km

▲ **Figure 8  Air masses approaching the UK**

▲ **Figure 9  Air mass descriptions**

## C   How does the weather affect us?

The weather has a huge impact on people's lives in the UK (Figure 10). The weather is particularly important for farmers. If the soil is too wet, or if it is frozen, it is hard to use machinery. Strong winds and heavy rain can flatten crops making them difficult to harvest. Sharp frosts in the late spring can damage fruit trees and bushes preventing fruit from growing. Very dry weather can cause crops to die.

▲ **Figure 10   How the weather affects us**

Supermarkets and other food shops are also affected by the weather. For example, a warm early summer leads to a huge demand for salad crops. Transport can be hit hard by poor weather, such as strong winds and snow. Even wet leaves blown onto railway lines can slow down trains! Heavy rain makes outdoor building work difficult and unpleasant.

Some people believe that the weather can affect our moods. Bright sunny weather is more likely to make us feel cheerful and positive whereas dark, damp and cold weather is more likely to make us feel miserable and depressed. What do you think?

Writers, artists and songwriters have been greatly influenced by the weather. The painter Claude Monet travelled to London in 1904 to see the effects of fog on sunlight (Figure 11).

▲ **Figure 11   Claude Monet *Houses of Parliament*; the effect of sunlight in the fog (1904)**

### Activities

6   Study the photos in Figure 10.

   a) For each photograph, identify the problems that have been caused by the weather.

   b) For one photograph, write a short story based on what is happening in the photograph. Describe how the weather has had an impact on a person/people in the photograph.

7   Study Figure 11.

   a) What effect has the fog had on sunlight in the picture?

   b) As a painter, why do you think Monet was interested in travelling to London to see the effect of fog?

   c) How else can fog affect people's lives? Think about the effect of fog on travel.

# D Extreme weather in the UK: Boscastle flash flood 2004

## Where is Boscastle?

Boscastle is a small village on the north coast of Cornwall (see the map in Figure 12). Originally it was a small fishing village centred on its harbour. Today, Boscastle is a very popular destination for tourists, particularly in the summer. Look at the photograph in Figure 13. It shows the narrow lanes in the harbour area. Notice that there are several quaint old buildings some of which are now shops.

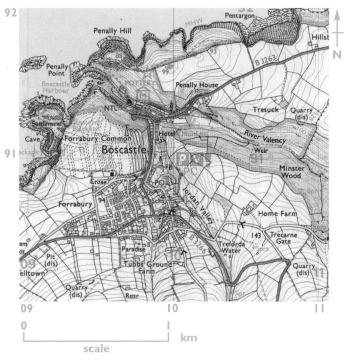

▲ **Figure 12   Map extract (1:25,000) of Boscastle**

### Activities

8  Study the map in Figure 12.

a) Give the four-figure grid reference of Boscastle harbour.

b) Most of the built up area of Boscastle is in what grid square?

c) What evidence is there that Boscastle is popular with tourists?

d) What is the six-figure grid reference of the youth hostel?

e) What is the meaning of the broken green line that follows the coast?

## What happened on 16 August 2004?

Monday 16 August dawned a typical summer's day and during the morning Boscastle quickly filled with day visitors. However, by lunchtime, storm clouds were gathering. During the afternoon, Boscastle was hit by a tremendous thunderstorm.

Over 1,422 million litres of rain fell in just two hours. This is equal to 21 petrol tanker loads of water flowing through Boscastle every second! The heavy rain swelled the normally small River Valency flowing towards the harbour causing it to burst its banks and flow over the adjacent car park.

The floodwaters quickly spread across the car park before surging down the narrow streets towards the harbour. Many cars were picked up and carried by the floodwaters. Together with tree trunks and large branches, the cars acted like battering rams smashing into bridges and buildings.

Can you see this building in Figure 15?

▲ **Figure 13   Boscastle before the flood**

41

Look at the photograph in Figure 14. It shows the car park shortly after the river burst its banks. Locate the car park on the map (Figure 12). The river normally flows from left to right behind the building. Notice how the car park is awash with water.

Look at the photograph in Figure 13. During the flood, the bridge and the road to the right were covered by water and buried beneath debris. The photograph in Figure 15 shows nearly the same area immediately after the flood. The bridge is beneath the pile of debris, cars and the tree!

## What were the effects of the flood?

The next day, the sheer scale of the devastation could be seen. The normally small river channel that flowed into the harbour was completely in-filled with sediment and debris. Huge tree trunks stuck out from the lower windows of shops. The contents of the shops had been swept away and deposited high up on the valley sides.

## Activities

9   Look at the photograph in Figure 14. Imagine that you were visiting Boscastle and that you took this photograph on your mobile phone. You have rung your best friend to report what is happening. Describe the scene in as much detail as possible.

10   Study the map extract in Figure 12 and the photograph in Figure 14.
   a)   Use the map in Figure 12 to give the six-figure grid reference of the car park.
   b)   Why do you think the car park was built here?
   c)   Why would the water have been able to flow very fast over the car park?
   d)   Notice that the valley sides are very steep. Why would this have increased the risk of flooding?

11   Spot the differences! Look carefully at the 'before' and 'after' photographs in Figures 13 and 15. Make a list of the changes that have taken place in the area shown on the photographs.

12   Look at the photograph in Figure 15. What do you think will need to be done to restore the area to what it used to look like before the flood?

River Valency normally flows from left to right behind this building

▲ **Figure 14   The car park area during the flood**

▲ **Figure 15   Boscastle harbour area immediately after the flood**

As the tide fell the following morning many cars were revealed in the harbour (see the photograph in Figure 16). Some had been completely flattened, whereas others were seemingly undamaged.

Remarkably nobody was killed, although a number of people had to be airlifted to safety. In all 58 buildings were flooded, four of which had to be demolished. Eighty-four wrecked cars were recovered from the harbour, and a further 32 were lost (presumably washed out to sea). The cost of damage to Boscastle and the surrounding area (where several roads and bridges were damaged) was estimated to be £2 million.

In the months that followed the event, buildings were dried out using large heaters and fans and a great deal of re-building took place. By the summer of 2005, several shops and businesses had re-opened and the tourists had returned.

▲ **Figure 16   Cars emerging in harbour**

## Activity

13  Study the photograph in Figure 16.

   **a)** How many cars have been dumped in the harbour by the flood?

   **b)** Describe the condition of the cars. How much damage have they suffered?

   **c)** The men in yellow are from the Fire Brigade's rescue service. What do you think they are doing?

   **d)** What does the photograph tell you about the force and power of the flood?

### ICT ACTIVITY

Use the information in this unit (together with material from the internet) to produce a newspaper front page about the Boscastle Flood of 2004. You will need to find some striking photographs to illustrate your account. Try to think of a powerful headline and take time to consider the design of your page.

Here are some useful websites that you can search:

http://www.tintagelweb.co.uk/BoscastleFlood.htm

http://news.bbc.co.uk/1/hi/in_pictures/3571748

http://en.wikipedia.org/wiki/Boscastle

# E   What is the climate of the UK?

The climate of the UK is the average weather over a period of 30 years. There are marked differences in the climate across the UK.

## Rainfall

Look at the map in Figure 17. Notice that the highest rainfall occurs in the west of the UK. If you live in the east of the UK, you will receive much less rainfall.

The main reason for this west–east split is because most of the time our weather comes from the west. As the air travels over the Atlantic Ocean it picks up huge quantities of water. On reaching the UK, the air is forced to rise up and over the mountains in the west, such as the Cambrian mountains in Wales. As the air rises, it cools. **Condensation** takes place, turning the water vapour into water droplets to form clouds and rain.

This type of rainfall is called **relief rainfall** ('relief' is a term used to describe the ups and downs of a landscape). When the air sinks on the other side of the mountains, it becomes drier and warmer. This sheltered and drier area is called the **rainshadow**.

Look at Figure 18. It is a sketch of the landscape of western Wales. The mountains in the diagram are the Cambrian Mountains. Notice how the mountains force the moist air to rise up to form clouds and rain. Figure 18 explains why there is a high rainfall total in this part of the UK (see the map in Figure 17).

**West**                                    **East**

CAMBRIAN
MOUNTAINS

▲ **Figure 18   Relief rainfall in West Wales**

## Activities

14 Study the map in Figure 17. You will need to use an atlas with this activity.
  a) Which parts of the British Isles have the highest rainfall?
  b) Use an atlas to locate and name a town or city that is located in the wettest part of the British Isles.
  c) What is the rainfall for Birmingham?
  d) Name a town that has a rainfall of less than 625 mm other than London.

15 Make a large careful copy of Figure 18. Add the following labels in their correct places to describe the formation of relief rainfall:
  ① ● warm moist air from the Atlantic Ocean
  ② ● air forced to rise up and over the mountains
  ③ ● condensation forms clouds and rain
  ④ ● drier warmer air sinks to the east of the mountains
  ⑤ ● rainshadow.

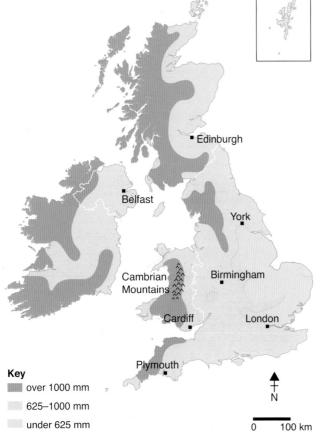

- Edinburgh

- Belfast

York -

Cambrian
Mountains         Birmingham -

Cardiff -         London -

Plymouth -

**Key**

▨ over 1000 mm

▨ 625–1000 mm

▨ under 625 mm

0     100 km

N

▲ **Figure 17   Average rainfall in the British Isles**

## Temperature

Just like rainfall, temperatures also vary across the UK. Look at the map in Figure 19, which shows winter temperatures in the UK. Notice that the highest temperatures are in the west and the southwest. The lowest temperatures are further east. The mountains in Scotland have particularly low temperatures.

The main reason for the west–east contrast in temperature is the wind direction. The most frequent or **prevailing wind** direction in the UK is from the southwest.

To the west of the UK a warm ocean current called the North Atlantic Drift sweeps warm water northwards from the Caribbean. Warmth from this ocean current is carried to the west of the UK by the prevailing wind. This results in warmer temperatures in the west of the UK. By the time these winds reach the eastern side of the UK they have lost some of the warmth. This is why temperatures are slightly cooler in the east.

The reason why the mountains of Scotland are very cold in the winter is because temperature decreases with height. The higher you are, the colder it gets. This explains why snow often falls in the mountains, but not on lower ground.

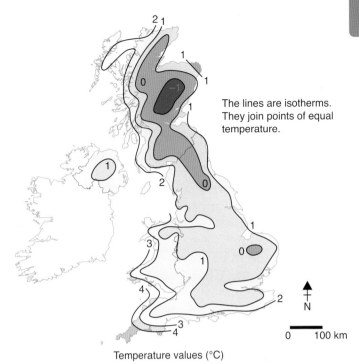

The lines are isotherms. They join points of equal temperature.

Temperature values (°C)

▲ **Figure 19  January average daily minimum temperatures, °C**

**Rucksack**

**Hat**
To prevent heat loss from head.

**Gloves or mittens**

**Warm underwear**
String vest, shirt and long-sleeved woollen pullover or tracksuit top.

**Windproof anorak**
With a hood, long enough to sit on, and with good long sleeves with no gaps for the wind to get in. Tight cuffs to keep out wind.

**Map, compass, whistle, route card**

**Long thick socks**
To turn trousers into breeches and protect legs.

**Trousers**
Cord, woollen or flannel (*not* jeans, they retain no heat when wet).

**Strong boots**
These must be comfortable and give support and protection. They should have good soles as you must be able to keep your grip.

**Thick woollen socks**
(Thin nylon socks can be both painful and dangerous.) Spare pairs required.

▲ **Figure 20   Mountain walking clothes**

### Activities

16  Study the map in Figure 19.
   a) What is the highest January temperature and where is it located?
   b) What is the name of the uplands that have a temperature of less than −1°C?
   c) Use the list of words below to write a few sentences describing why the temperatures are lower in the east than in the west.
      Atlantic Ocean   prevailing winds
      North Atlantic Drift   colder   west
      warmer   east
   d) Why do some people choose to retire to coastal towns in southwest England?
   e) Imagine that you are a farmer in Cornwall growing new potatoes and daffodils in early spring. Why would you be keen to sell your produce to people living in the east of the UK?

17  Figure 20 shows a girl dressed to go walking in the Scottish mountains in the winter. Look back to the various maps and diagrams to remind you of the typical weather conditions in Scotland at this time of year.
   a) Do you think she is dressed sensibly? Explain your answer.
   b) Suggest the items that the girl should pack in her rucksack before she sets out.

Look at Figure 21 to see the pattern of summer temperatures in the UK. Notice that there is a clear north–south split with the north being cooler than the south. There are two main reasons for this. Firstly, the sun is slightly higher in the sky in southern England and is therefore more powerful. Secondly, southern England is more commonly affected by the warmer air masses sweeping up from the south. These warmer air masses do not always reach the north of the UK.

## Activities

18  Study the map in Figure 21.
   a) The range of temperature is the difference between the highest and the lowest temperature. What is the temperature range in the UK in July from the lowest isotherm to the highest isotherm?
   b) Use an atlas to locate the parts of the UK with the highest July temperatures.
   c) Where are the lowest July temperatures in the UK?

19  Study Figure 22.
   a) What evidence is there from the photograph that there has been a shortage of rainfall in the past few months?
   b) How do you think the weather in the photograph might be making the situation worse?
   c) Where do you think the normal level of the reservoir is? Explain your answer.
   d) What local ecosystems in the photograph might be suffering from a  shortage of water?
   e) Suggest how one of the ecosystems you have identified might be suffering.
   f) If the climate of the UK changes to become drier and hotter in the summer, water shortages could become a real issue. Can you suggest ways that people might conserve water in the summer to reduce demand?

The lines are isotherms. They join points of equal temperature.

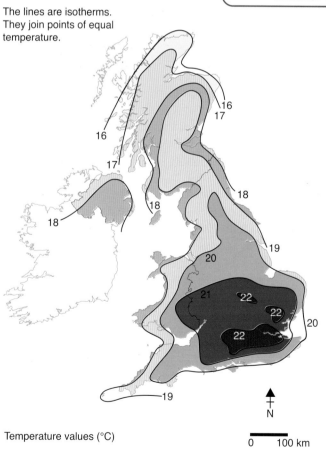

Temperature values (°C)

0    100 km

▲ Figure 21  July average daily maximum temperatures

▲ Figure 22  Low water at Ogden Water Reservoir

# Climate graphs

Climate data is commonly displayed in the form of a **climate graph**. Figure 23 contains climate data for York and Plymouth. Both towns are located on Figure 17 (see page 44). A climate graph for York has been drawn in Figure 24. Notice that York is located in the drier east of the UK. On a climate graph the rainfall figures are drawn as bars. The temperature values are drawn as lines above the bars.

## York

| Month | Average daily minimum temperature (°C) | Average daily maximum temperature (°C) | Average monthly rainfall (mm) |
|---|---|---|---|
| Jan | 1 | 6 | 59 |
| Feb | 1 | 7 | 46 |
| March | 2 | 10 | 37 |
| April | 4 | 13 | 41 |
| May | 7 | 16 | 50 |
| June | 10 | 19 | 50 |
| July | 12 | 21 | 62 |
| Aug | 12 | 21 | 68 |
| Sept | 10 | 18 | 55 |
| Oct | 7 | 14 | 56 |
| Nov | 4 | 10 | 65 |
| Dec | 2 | 7 | 50 |

## Plymouth

| Month | Average daily minimum temperature (°C) | Average daily maximum temperature (°C) | Average monthly rainfall (mm) |
|---|---|---|---|
| Jan | 4 | 8 | 99 |
| Feb | 4 | 8 | 74 |
| March | 5 | 10 | 69 |
| April | 6 | 12 | 53 |
| May | 8 | 15 | 63 |
| June | 11 | 18 | 53 |
| July | 13 | 19 | 70 |
| Aug | 13 | 19 | 77 |
| Sept | 12 | 18 | 78 |
| Oct | 9 | 15 | 91 |
| Nov | 7 | 11 | 113 |
| Dec | 5 | 9 | 110 |

(Source: World Weather Book Hutchinson)

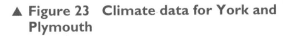

▲ **Figure 23   Climate data for York and Plymouth**

## Activities

20  Study Figures 23 and 24.

a) Use the climate data in Figure 23 to draw two climate graphs, one for York and the other for Plymouth. Use the same vertical scale for both graphs to enable you to compare the two finished graphs.

b) Write the following labels onto the graphs that you have just drawn. They describe the impact of the climate on the lives of two children. You have to decide which graph they should go on and where.

● 'Heavy rainfall in the winter makes the ground very wet and muddy when I ride my horse.'

● 'The mild winters mean I can let my horse stay outside most of the time.'

● 'My dad has to scrape the ice off the car in the winter.'

● 'We have a lot of rain throughout the year, which is why the fields are always so green.'

● 'Summers are very warm. Great for cricket!'

● 'Sometimes we have heavy rainstorms in the summer, which stop me playing cricket.'

c) Write a few sentences to compare the two climates.

d) Would you prefer to live in York or Plymouth? Explain your answer.

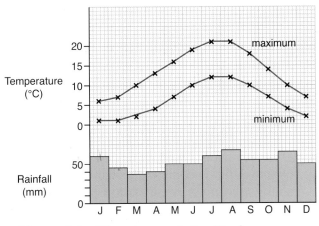

▲ **Figure 24   Climate graph for York**

## F  Issue: Is there any evidence for climate change in the UK?

Most scientists agree that global warming is happening across the world. You have probably heard of the concerns about melting ice caps, sea levels rising and increasing problems of droughts and floods.

Many of the world's environments are changing. Plants and animals (for which these environments are their natural habitats) are under threat. Have you heard of the plight of the polar bears, for example (Figure 4 page 37)?

But what about the UK? Is there any evidence of climate change here?

To find out more about this issue you are going to conduct an enquiry. Look back to page 4 to remind yourself of the stages of an enquiry.

### How to do your enquiry

To carry out your enquiry you should work in small groups of three or four people.

Start by reading the 'Aims of the enquiry' so that you know what you are expected to do.

Decide as a group how you are going to carry out your enquiry. Who is going to do what? Also, decide how you are going to present your enquiry. You could produce a written report, a poster or a PowerPoint presentation. You might choose to do something more ambitious such as making use of mobile phones or video clips. It is up to your group to decide.

### Aims of the enquiry

There are three separate parts to this enquiry.

● To discover what evidence there is for climate change in the UK.

● To decide if the evidence is credible and reliable. Does it come from well-known and reliable people or organisations?

● To suggest whether any changes are really a problem. Do the changes matter? Is all change bad?

### Where can I find information for the enquiry?

There are four main places where you can find evidence for climate change in the UK:

● look at the information in Figure 25

● library research: ask your school librarian for some help (remember that because this is a recent issue, you will need to refer to relatively recently published books)

● internet research: if using Google, click the 'UK' button to restrict your searches (stick to recognised organisations such as the RSPB and the BBC); be specific with your searches

● your teacher.

### Is the UK's climate changing?

In recent years there appears to be evidence of a change in the UK's climate.

● The 1990s was the warmest decade in central England since records began in the 1660s.

● The growing season for plants in central England has lengthened by about one month since 1900.

● In the UK and elsewhere, there is evidence that spring in particular is getting earlier in the year. Daffodils are blooming during months that used to be considered to be mid-winter. Crocus bulbs are flowering twice a year, in autumn as well as early spring. Birds are laying their eggs earlier. Scientists call this 'season creep'.

● Heatwaves have become more frequent in summer.

● Winters over the last 200 years have become much wetter relative to summers throughout the UK. There are now fewer frosts and winter cold spells.

● The average sea level around the UK is now about 10 cm higher than it was in 1900.

*(see http://www.ukcip.org.uk/climate_change/how_uk_change.asp*

*for further details)*

▲ Figure 25  Is the UK's climate changing?

# The Physical Landscape

## CHAPTER 4

**In this chapter you will study:**

- landscapes in the UK
- weathering and erosion
- limestone landscapes of the Yorkshire Dales
- quarrying in the Peak District.

# A   Landscapes in the UK

We are very lucky in the UK to have a great variety of landscapes to enjoy (Figure 1).

Much of England, southern Scotland and Northern Ireland is made up of rolling landscapes with hills and valleys. This land is mostly used for farming crops (arable farming) or keeping animals (pastoral farming).

The main mountains in the UK are found in North Wales, the English Lake District and much of western and northern Scotland (Figure 2). In these areas the high land and steep slopes make it difficult for arable farming. Soils tend to be thin and rocky and the climate is harsh, with strong winds and high rainfall. Sheep grazing and forestry tend to be the main land uses. The mountains of the UK are very popular with tourists who enjoy walking and mountain biking.

▲ **Figure 1   a) South Downs   b) The Peak District   c) Ben Nevis**

# B    Why does the landscape vary in the UK?

Imagine digging a hole in your garden or in your school playing fields. First you would dig through grass and then through soil. Then you would hit the solid rocks below. It is the rocks that lie under our feet that create the great variety of landscapes in the UK.

The mountains in the UK are made of very tough rocks. These rocks resist the forces of nature, such as rivers. They are worn away very slowly over thousands of years. The rocks that form the lowland areas are much weaker and are much more easily worn away.

## ICT ACTIVITY

There are several internet sites such as 'flickr' where people can upload photos of their home areas. Create your own version at school by uploading a photo of your favourite landscape. Write a few words to explain your choice.

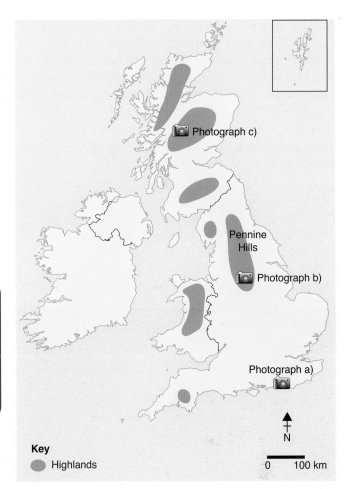

▶ **Figure 2   Highland areas in the UK**

---

## Activities

1   Study the photographs in Figure 1.

   a) For each photograph write down some words that describe the landscape. The words can be things that you can see or words that describe how you feel about each landscape.

   b) For one of the landscapes in Figure 1 use your list of words to write a Haiku poem (see page 15) or a wordscape (words arranged on a page to reflect the shape of the landscape).

   c) You have been asked to choose one of the landscapes to visit on holiday. Write a postcard from your chosen area saying what you like about it. The postcard can be to your family or a friend.

2   Figure 2 is a map of the UK showing the main highland areas. The locations of the three photographs in Figure 1 are also shown on the map.

   a) Make a copy of the uplands in Figure 2 on a blank outline map. Use a brown colour to shade the upland areas.

   b) Use an atlas to help you label the following highland areas on your map:
   ● English Lake District        ● Exmoor
   ● Dartmoor
   ● Cambrian Mountains
   ● Southern Uplands
   ● North West Highlands
   ● Grampian Mountains.

   c) Locate and label your home town on your map.

   d) Give your map a title.

## C Weathering and erosion

**Weathering** is the slow breakdown or decay of rocks. It is called weathering because it often involves aspects of the weather (such as rain and hot or cold temperatures). **Erosion** is different from weathering in that it involves rocks being carried away by natural forces (such as rivers, glaciers and the sea). Together weathering and erosion are responsible for wearing away the landscape.

Look at Figure 3. It is a limestone gargoyle that was originally part of St Paul's cathedral in London. Notice how its features are no longer sharply defined. This is because its surface has decayed due to weathering.

When rainwater passes through the air it absorbs gases such as carbon dioxide. This makes the rainwater more acidic than it is naturally. When the rain lands on the limestone gargoyle, a chemical change takes place, causing the rock to slowly dissolve. This is an example of a chemical weathering process called **carbonation**.

Now look at Figure 4. The huge pile of rocks at the bottom of the cliff is called a **scree slope**. The jagged rock fragments have fallen from the cliff above. The process that has caused this to happen is called **freeze-thaw**. Figure 5 describes how the process works.

There are many different types of erosion (Figure 6). You will look in more detail at processes of river erosion later in this chapter. You will come across other forms of erosion later in the series.

▲ **Figure 3   Limestone gargoyle**

▲ **Figure 4   Scree slope and cliff face**

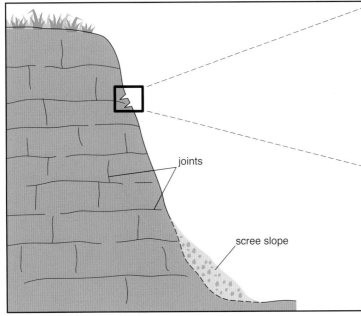

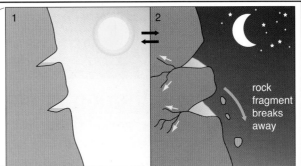

1    Water collects in cracks in the rock.

2  • Water freezes and becomes ice when temperatures
      drop to 0°C and below.
   • The ice exerts pressure on the rock expanding
      the cracks.
   • With changes in temperature repeated cycles of
      freezing and thawing eventually cause rock fragments
      to break away to form a scree slope.

▲ **Figure 5   Freeze-thaw process**

## Activities

3  Study Figure 4.

   a) Do you think freeze-thaw is
      happening on the rock
      outcrop? Give reasons for your
      answer.

   b) What information about the
      climate would you want to find
      out to confirm that
      freeze-thaw was occurring
      here in the present day?

   c) Look at the block of rock on
      the cliff labelled A. How will the
      process of freeze-thaw lead to
      this piece of rock eventually
      breaking away from the cliff?
      Use a diagram or storyboard to
      help you in your answer.

4  Study Figure 6. Look closely at
   the photographs and discuss in
   pairs the following questions.

   a) Look at waves crashing
      against the cliff. How do you
      think the sea is eroding the
      cliff?

   b) Glaciers are able to carry out a
      great deal of erosion. Why do
      you think this is?

   c) Wind on its own is not able to
      erode rocks in the desert.
      What do you think is needed
      for wind erosion to take place?

▲ **Figure 6   Erosion by sea, wind and ice**

## LOCAL FIELDWORK

## Studying weathering at school

**Figure 7 shows some typical features of weathering on the side of a school building. Notice how the surface is pitted and flaking. See how the cement has started to crumble.**

Take a walk around your school grounds to see if you can find any evidence of weathering on the buildings. Look particularly at the bottom of walls where water often collects to increase the rate of weathering. Take a photograph and add labels to describe the evidence of weathering that you have discovered. Use Figure 7 to help you.

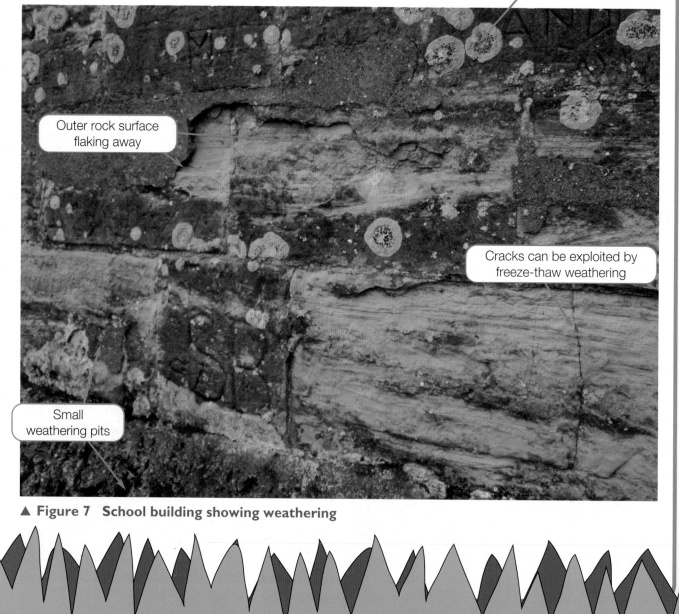

Lichens can secrete acids encouraging weathering

Outer rock surface flaking away

Cracks can be exploited by freeze-thaw weathering

Small weathering pits

▲ **Figure 7 School building showing weathering**

# D   Limestone landscapes: the Yorkshire Dales

**Limestone** is one of the most common rocks in the UK. It is a tough grey-coloured rock that typically forms upland areas, such as the Pennine Hills (Figure 2, page 51).

Look at Figure 8. This is a photograph of a typical limestone landscape in the Yorkshire Dales in the northern part of the Pennine Hills. Notice the bare rocky outcrops on the hillsides, the steep-sided valleys and the sheep pastures. Weathering is very active on limestone causing it to dissolve. Very little rock material remains after weathering has taken place, which means that the soil on limestone is very thin.

One of the most amazing things about limestone landscapes is what can be found underground! Deep within the limestone, water seeping through the rock slowly enlarges the many cracks to form massive **caverns** (Figure 9). Within these caverns can be found the most magical features of limestone landscapes, **stalactites** and **stalagmites**.

Water dripping through the rock is rich in chemicals dissolved from the limestone. In the caverns, the drops of water deposit tiny amounts of solid calcite on the roof. Drip by drip, the deposits grow like icicles hanging down from the roof. These are stalactites. The drips that land on the floor of the cavern also deposit calcite, but this grows upwards to form stumpy stalagmites. Occasionally a stalactite joins with a stalagmite to form a magnificent column (Figure 9). Columns such as those in Figure 9 take thousands of years to form.

▲ **Figure 8   Watlowes, Yorkshire Dales**

▲ **Figure 9   Limestone cavern with stalactites, stalagmites and columns**

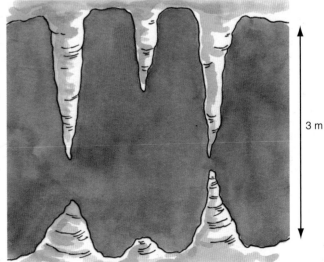

3 m

▲ **Figure 10   Stalactites and stalagmites**

## Activities

5 Study Figure 8 (page 55).

  a) Write a few sentences to describe the landscape in the photograph.

  b) Do you think the weathering process of carbonation will be taking place in this landscape? Why?

  c) Do you think the process of freeze-thaw will be occurring? Why?

  d) What type of farming would you expect here and why?

  e) Would you like to visit this landscape? Give reasons for your answer.

6 Study Figure 10 (page 55), which shows stalactites and stalagmites in a cave. You have been asked to produce a diagram to be mounted on an information board at the entrance to the cave. Work through the following steps to create your diagram. Use a sheet of plain paper for this activity.

  a) Copy the diagram and add labels to identify the following features:
  ● stalactite
  ● stalagmite.

  b) Draw onto your diagram where you think a column is most likely to form.

  c) Draw blue arrows to show how water drips to the tip of the stalactite and then drips on the floor of the cavern to form the stalagmite.

  d) Add labels or a written commentary to describe how these features are formed.

7 Study Figure 12. Work with your neighbour in this activity.

  a) Sometimes local people object to quarries. Can you think of some reasons why?

  b) Now try to suggest some possible benefits that quarrying might bring to the local area.

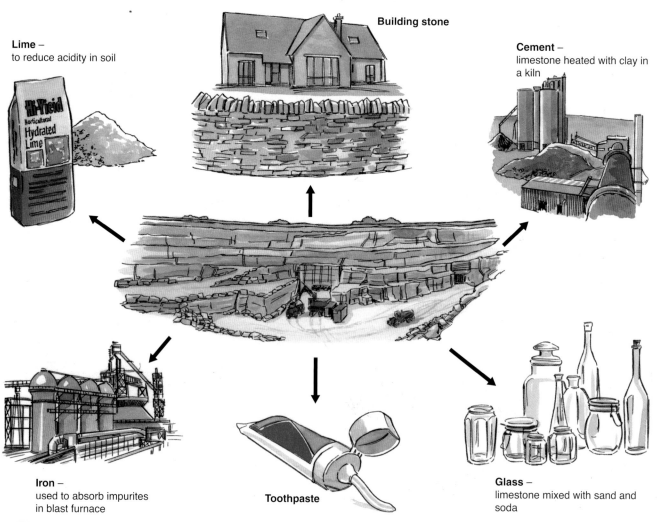

Lime –
to reduce acidity in soil

Building stone

Cement –
limestone heated with clay in a kiln

Iron –
used to absorb impurites in blast furnace

Toothpaste

Glass –
limestone mixed with sand and soda

▲ Figure 11   Uses of limestone

Limestone is a very useful rock and there are often quarries in limestone areas to extract the rock (Figure 12). Explosives are used to blast the rock apart. It is then crushed in a powerful crushing mill before being transported away to make cement or to make a range of other products, such as toothpaste (see Figure 11)!

### ICT ACTIVITY

For this activity you will need to work in small groups. Your group, or 'team' has been asked to market and promote Wensleydale in the Yorkshire Dales to people living elsewhere in the UK. Choose one of the following methods of marketing:

- a promotional poster to be displayed in Tourist Information Centres across the UK

- a small booklet advertising the attractions of Wensleydale

- a PowerPoint or Movie Maker presentation.

Use the internet to discover some of the attractions of the area.  A good site to start with is http://www.wensleydale.org/index.shtml. Include a map and as many illustrations as you can. Don't forget to think of a catchy title. If you are using PowerPoint or Movie Maker you could record a voiceover to explain the area's attractions to your audience. Think about what tourists would like to visit and find out about.

## E   Issue: Should a new limestone quarry be opened on Longstone Edge?

### Background

Longstone Edge is a limestone ridge situated in the Peak District about 15 miles southwest of Sheffield. Since the 1950s quarries have been cut into the landscape (Figure 12) in search of minerals such as fluorspar (used for making glass, chemicals and plastics) and lead (used in batteries and building). To begin with, the limestone was a waste product because the minerals were more valuable. However, more recently, the limestone itself has become a valuable material and increasing amounts have been quarried.

The Peak District is a National Park. It is an attractive upland area popular with visitors. Developments such as quarrying are carefully managed to avoid the landscape becoming damaged. You are going to investigate a proposal for a new quarry in the area.

▼ Figure 12   Quarry, Yorkshire Dales

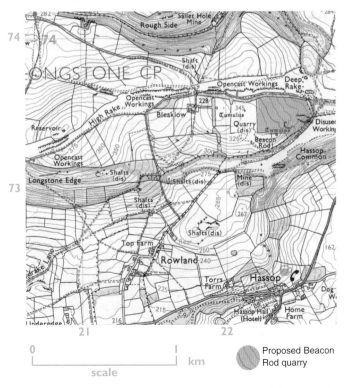

Proposed Beacon Rod quarry

▲ Figure 13   Quarry site at Beacon Rod 1:25,000

## Activity

### Beacon Rod Public Enquiry

For the purpose of this activity we are going to imagine that a site called Beacon Rod (see Figure 14) is due to become a limestone quarry. Some people are in favour of this development but others are fiercely against it. The local planning authority has decided to hold a Public Enquiry to discuss the issues before a decision is made.

▲ Figure 14  Longstone Edge

Divide up the class to represent the following interest groups:

- the RSPB
- the Peak District National Park Authority
- the owners of the land
- local residents
- owner of a local haulage company
- local shop owner

Four or five people in the class should form the public enquiry judges (they will hear the evidence, ask questions and eventually make a decision).

**Interest groups:** Use the information in this section (together with internet research) to build up a case for or against the proposal. Be prepared to answer questions from the judges.

**Judges:** Conduct your own background research into the proposal. You will have to make the final decision so you should be well informed. Put together some questions to ask the interest groups.

**The public enquiry:** When the cases have been written, conduct a public enquiry in your classroom. Begin with the speakers in favour of the development. Then let the opponents put their case forward. The judges will eventually have to make a decision based on the evidence they have heard. They can ask questions to the various interest groups.

Information about Longstone Edge can be found at: http://www.longstone-edge.org.uk /theproblem/index.htm.

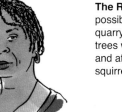

**The RSPB** are concerned about the possible damage to wildlife habitats if quarrying takes place. Plants, shrubs and trees will be removed destroying habitats and affecting wildlife (including birds, squirrels, foxes, rabbits and badgers).

**The Peak District National Park Authority** oversees developments in the National Park. It is responsible for protecting and conserving the countryside and encouraging visitors to the area. The Authority is concerned that quarrying will spoil and pollute the landscape and cause problems for local people, such as damage to roads, noise and traffic congestion.

**The owners of the land** want to develop the site to extract limestone and fluorspar. These materials are much in demand for a range of industrial uses. They suggest that the quarry will bring jobs and wealth to the area. They plan to extract the rock behind woodland screens, so that the quarry is not an eyesore. When quarrying stops, they will restore the site with grass and trees, and plan to turn the area into a nature reserve.

**Jack Sprout, a local resident,** is concerned about the noise and dust created by the quarrying. He is not alone. Many of the nearby residents are against the proposal. They are also concerned about the large lorries that will use the narrow country lanes, damaging the grass verges and making the roads dirty and potholed.

**Peter Rabbelt, owner of a local haulage company** is in favour of the project because his lorries will be used to transport the rock. He expects to be able to employ several more drivers and feels that the quarry will bring money into the local area.

**Angela Muffin, local shopkeeper** is also in favour of the quarry. She thinks that, with extra employment in the area, more people will use her shop. At the moment she is just surviving and any extra income would be very welcome.

▲ Figure 15  Interest groups

# River Landscapes

**In this chapter you will study:**

- river landscapes of the River Exe, Devon
- river processes
- river landforms
- river fieldwork
- sustainable river management.

## A  The River Exe, Devon

In this chapter you are going to study some of the processes and landforms associated with rivers. To do this you are going to focus on one river – the River Exe in southwest England (see the map in Figure 2).

The River Exe has its **source** (the point where it starts) high up in the hills of Exmoor in Somerset (see Figure 1, and its location in Figure 2). From here it flows for some 100 km in a southerly direction through the county of Devon until it reaches the south coast at Exmouth. The River Exe flows through the city of Exeter before reaching the sea.

▲ **Figure I   The River Exe near its source at Exhead, Exmoor**

### Activities

1  Study the photograph in Figure 1. It was taken very near to the source of the River Exe.
   a)  Describe the landscape in the photograph.
   b)  Select words from the following list to write a sentence describing the river:
       deep  shallow  clear  polluted  wide
   c)  If you were to visit the river here, would you wear wellies or trainers on your feet? Explain your answer.
   d)  What type of farming would you expect to take place in this area and why?
2  Study Figure 2.
   a)  What name is given to the start of a river?
   b)  What is the name of the first village that the River Exe flows through?
   c)  What name is given to the point where two rivers join?
   d)  Locate Wimbleball Reservoir. What is a reservoir and what is its purpose?
   e)  Lots of smaller rivers join the River Exe. What name is given to a stream that joins a larger river?
   f)  The M5 crosses the River Exe to the north of Exeter. True or false?
   g)  What is the straight-line distance between Exeter and Exmouth?

The River Exe played an important role in the growth of Exeter. In medieval times, water powered mills produced paper and textiles (cloth). Raw materials were brought into Exeter by boat for processing. The finished products were then transported away to the English Channel and beyond.

Today, the river is still important, but it is mostly used for leisure and recreation (including water sports, bird watching and walking).

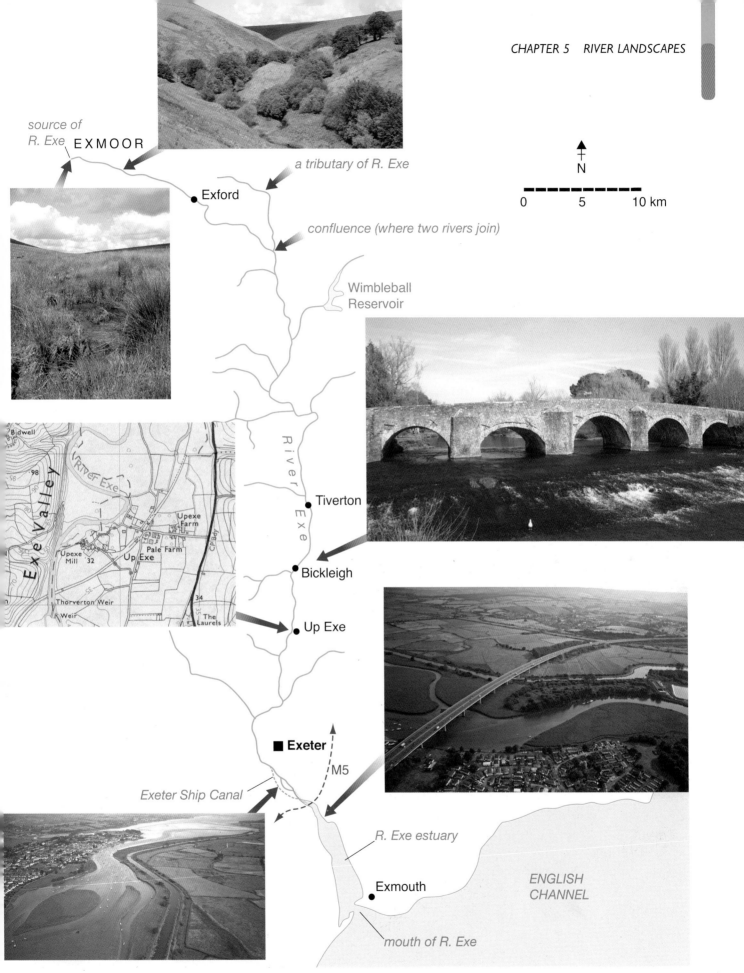

source of
R. Exe **E X M O O R**

*a tributary of R. Exe*

● Exford

*confluence (where two rivers join)*

Wimbleball
Reservoir

River
Exe

Exe Valley

Bidwell

River Exe

Upexe
Farm

Upexe
Mill   32   Up Exe

Pale Farm

Thorverton Weir

Weir

The
Laurels

N

0          5          10 km

● Tiverton

● Bickleigh

● Up Exe

■ **Exeter**

M5

Exeter Ship Canal

*R. Exe estuary*

● Exmouth

*mouth of R. Exe*

ENGLISH
CHANNEL

▲ **Figure 2   The course of the River Exe**

## B   River processes

As water flows down a river it carries out three major processes. They are transportation, erosion and deposition.

- **Transportation:** There are four types of sediment transportation. **Traction** is when larger rocks on the riverbed are slowly rolled along the bed. **Saltation** is when slightly smaller particles move along the bed in a bouncing manner. **Suspension** is when smaller, lighter rock particles are picked up and carried by the river. **Solution** is when some rocks are dissolved in the water and carried invisibly downstream.

- **Erosion:** When the water is flowing fast (for example, after a period of heavy rain), it may carry out erosion of its bank or bed. Look at

the photograph in Figure 3. Notice how the force of the water has undercut the riverbank on the lefthand side and caused it to collapse. Notice how the collapse has caused the river to split into three smaller channels.

- **Deposition:** When the flow of a river slows down it will deposit the sediment it is carrying. By the time the River Exe reaches the sea, it has picked up and transported a huge amount of sediment. As it gets close to the sea, the river becomes tidal. This interferes with the flow of the river and causes rapid deposition (the river drops what it has been carrying), forming the sandbanks and mudflats you can see in the photograph in Figure 5.

▲ **Figure 3   River with collapsed bank**

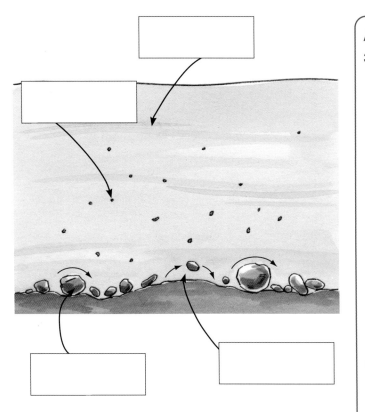

▲ Figure 4   River sediment transport

## Activities

3   Study Figure 3.

   a)   What evidence is there that the riverbank on the left has recently collapsed?

   b)   Notice that the river channel has split into three. In which channel do you think the water is flowing fastest? Why?

   c)   How do you think the river channel will change in the future? Explain your answer.

   d)   Many of the pebbles on the riverbed have smooth edges. How do you think erosion has caused the pebbles to become smoother?

   e)   What do you think the landowner should do to prevent people standing too close to the edge of the riverbank?

   f)   Do you think something should be done to stop the erosion or should nature be left to take its own course? Give reasons for your answer.

4   Make a copy of Figure 4, which shows the different ways that a river can transport sediment.

   Add the following labels in their correct places:

   ● traction – larger sediment rolled on the river bed

   ● saltation – sediment is bounced on the river bed

   ● suspension – smaller sediment picked up and carried by the river

   ● solution – sediment dissolved in the river.

▲ Figure 5   Oblique aerial photo of Exe estuary

## C River landforms

Look at the photograph in Figure 6. It shows the River Exe and its valley close to Exford (see Figure 2, page 61). The river, now wider and deeper than in Figure 1, has carved a deep and steep-sided **V-shaped valley**. The land is mainly grassland and is mostly used for grazing sheep.

By the time the river reaches Bickleigh (see Figure 2), it is quite different (see the photograph in Figure 8). The river channel is much wider and deeper. This is because many smaller rivers or **tributaries** have joined and there is now much more water flowing down the river. The valley itself is now several kilometres wide. The land is used for settlements, roads and for farming.

▲ **Figure 6   River Exe showing river and V-shaped valley**

### Activity

5 Figure 7 is a sketch of the photograph in Figure 6.

  a) Have a go at drawing your own sketch of the photograph. Add labels to describe the main features of the river and its valley.

  b) Why do you think this landscape is used for sheep grazing rather than for growing crops?

  c) There are many footpaths and bridleways in the area. Why do you think it is so popular with walkers and horse riders?

▲ **Figure 7   Sketch of the photograph in Figure 6**

As the river nears Exeter it forms a series of curves or bends. These are called **meanders**. There are some excellent meanders near the village of Up Exe (see the map in Figure 9). Look at Figure 11 to find out what happens at a meander.

▲ Figure 8   River Exe at Bickleigh

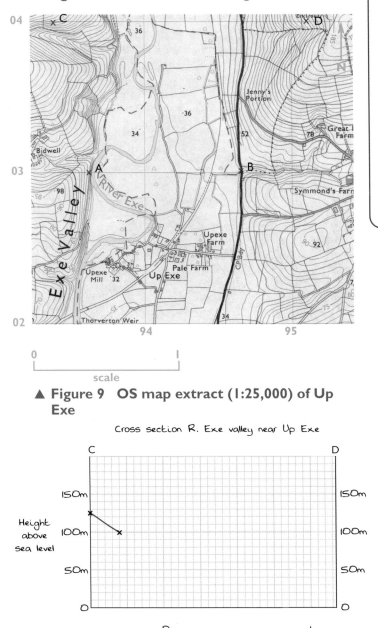

0 [scale]

▲ Figure 9   OS map extract (1:25,000) of Up Exe

## Activity

6  Study Figure 9.

   a)  What is the contour interval on the map?

   b)  Locate the 03 grid line. What height contour marks the lowest edge of the river valley along this grid line?

   c)  Measure the distance in km across the river's **floodplain** from A to B.

   d)  Do you think the river will be eroding the edge of the valley at A? Explain your answer. (Hint – look at Figure 11).

   e)  Do you think Up Exe is at risk from flooding? Explain your answer.

   f)  The black broken line that runs close to the river is a district boundary. When it was first drawn, it ran down the centre of the river. Can you suggest why it no longer does so in places?

   g)  On a copy of Figure 10 complete the cross-section across the river valley (from the 125 m contour at C to the 150 m contour at D). Label the river, the floodplain and the valley.

Cross section R. Exe valley near Up Exe

▲ Figure 10   Axes for cross-section

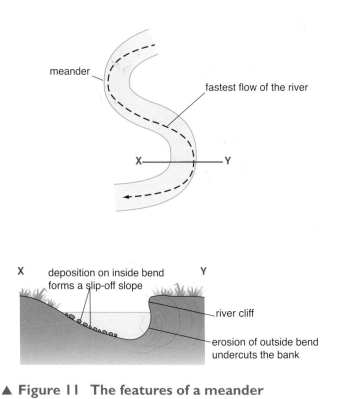

▲ Figure 11   The features of a meander

**65**

Beyond Exeter, the river is very wide and deep (Figure 12). Running alongside is the Exeter Ship Canal, which was built to make the city more accessible by ship. Opened in 1539, it is the oldest post-Roman canal in England. The bridge that you can see in the photograph carries the motorway over the river. The river itself is now influenced by the daily tides – it has become a tidal river. The tides interfere with the flow of the river causing huge quantities of sediment to be deposited in the river **estuary** forming sand banks and mudflats.

The estuary gradually opens out to Exmouth where the River Exe finally ends its journey in the English Channel. This is the **mouth** of the river.

## Activity

7 Study Figure 12. Use Figure 2, page 61 to help you answer the following questions.
  a) In what direction is the photograph looking?
  b) Which of the two river channels **A** and **B** is the Exeter Ship Canal?
  c) What is the motorway bridging the River Exe?
  d) What is the evidence that deposition has taken place in the river?
  e) What do you think are the white specs in the river to the left of the photograph?
  f) Why do you think the houses facing the river at **C** are popular?
  g) What do you think the land is used for at **D**?
  h) A housing company wants to build a new housing estate but can't decide whether to build it at **X** or **Y**. Which site do you think is best and why?

▲ **Figure 12  Oblique aerial photo of Exe below Exeter**

# LOCAL FIELDWORK

**Small rivers are excellent for carrying out fieldwork. You do, however, need to be careful when working near water. Pebbles can be slippery and riverbanks can collapse. Never go into the water unless directed by a teacher. The water may be polluted, so always wash your hands before eating.**

1   **Investigate the changes that take place between two or more sites down a river.**

Find out if the following statements or hypotheses are true for your river.

- *The cross-sectional area of a river increases with distance downstream. This is because tributaries add more and more water to a river.*

Use a tape measure and metre rule to measure the width and depth of the river (Figure 13). Present this information in the form of a cross profile of the river. You could then calculate the cross-sectional area of the river (width x average depth).

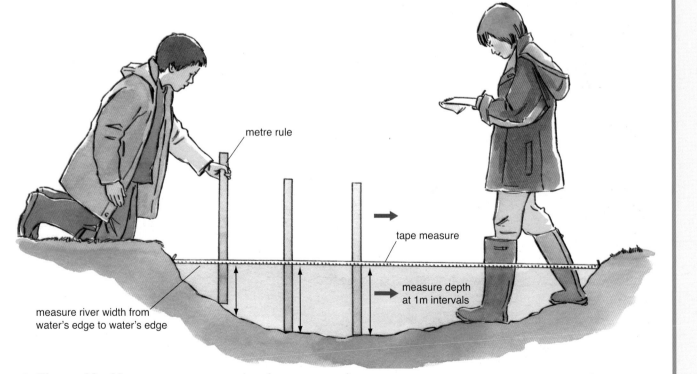

metre rule

tape measure

measure depth at 1m intervals

measure river width from water's edge to water's edge

▲ **Figure 13   How to measure a river's cross-section**

# LOCAL FIELDWORK

● *Rivers flow faster with distance downstream.*
*(The flow of a river is its velocity.)*

You can measure the velocity simply by recording the time taken for a float (an orange is ideal) to travel a set distance, say 5 metres. Divide the distance travelled by the time taken to give you a velocity in metres per second.
You should repeat the process several times to give you an average velocity for a particular site.

● *Pebbles become smaller and more rounded with distance downstream. As pebbles are transported the process of* **attrition** *makes them smaller and more rounded.*

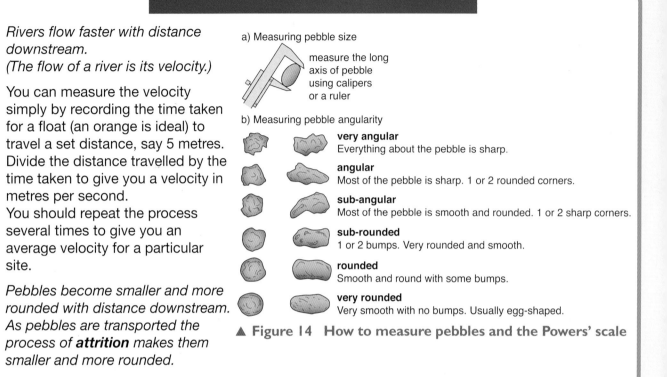

a) Measuring pebble size

measure the long axis of pebble using calipers or a ruler

b) Measuring pebble angularity

**very angular**
Everything about the pebble is sharp.

**angular**
Most of the pebble is sharp. 1 or 2 rounded corners.

**sub-angular**
Most of the pebble is smooth and rounded. 1 or 2 sharp corners.

**sub-rounded**
1 or 2 bumps. Very rounded and smooth.

**rounded**
Smooth and round with some bumps.

**very rounded**
Very smooth with no bumps. Usually egg-shaped.

▲ **Figure 14   How to measure pebbles and the Powers' scale**

Take a sample of 30 pebbles chosen randomly from the bed of the river. Measure and record the long axis of each pebble and assess its angularity using the Powers' scale (Figure 14). This information can be presented as a pie chart. You can calculate the average pebble size to compare with other sites along the river.

## 2  How can the river environment be improved?

● In this activity you will need to work in small groups. Locate and visit a short stretch of river in or close to an urban area. The aim of this activity is to identify the uses of the river and suggest ways that the environment could be improved for people who wish to visit it.

● Look for evidence of different uses of the river and its immediate environment. Are there any footpaths? Do people walk along the riverbank? Is the river used for fishing or boating? Is there much wildlife evident?

● Now think how the river environment could be improved. Consider new or improved paths. Can the riverbank be made more accessible? Should there be benches and litter bins? What about a bird hide?

Plot your ideas on a plan of the area and illustrate with photographs.

# D   Issue: How can rivers be managed sustainably?

People have altered rivers in the UK to control their shape, improve navigation or reduce the risk of flooding. Concrete has replaced plants along riverbanks, and the amount and variety of wildlife has declined. Meanders have been cut off to create artificially-straight channels. In towns and cities, rivers are often dirty and polluted. Maintaining artificial channels that work against natural river processes is expensive and non-sustainable.

Today there is an increasing desire to return rivers to their natural courses to make them more **sustainable**. The natural river processes of erosion and deposition are being encouraged. Plants and trees are being planted to encourage wildlife back into the river ecosystem. Natural-looking rivers are more appealing to people for walking, picnicking or simply sitting and relaxing. This type of sustainable river management is called **river restoration**.

Look at Figure 15. It shows the River Marden in the town centre of Calne, Wiltshire. Compare this photograph with Figure 16. The changes are quite dramatic! The main difference is that the previously-straight channel has been replaced with a more natural-looking meandering channel. Access to the river is easier and the environment is more attractive.

## Activity

8  Study Figures 15 and 16.

   a)  Working in pairs, make a list of the changes that have taken place to the river channel and its immediate environment.

   b)  What has been done to encourage people to spend time near the river?

   c)  Why might people wish to spend more time close to the river?

   d)  How do you think the area will change over a period of five years?

   e)  Is there anything you would do to improve the area further?

▲ Figure 15   River Marden – before works (River Restoration Centre)

▲ Figure 16   River Marden – after works (River Restoration Centre)

## Activity

9  Study Figure 17. It shows a stretch of the River Avon in Salisbury, Wiltshire. Here the river is running through an area of parkland. A decision has been made to restore the river and improve its environment. You have been asked to come up with a plan for river restoration. In your plan you need to address the following aspects:

- the straight channel should be replaced with a meandering channel
- the hard concrete river edge should be more natural
- bushes and trees should be planted to encourage wildlife into the area
- facilities should be provided for people wishing to spend time near the river, such as seats and litter bins.

a) Use a sketch, a map, or a tracing to suggest the changes that you would make to the river.

b) Add detailed labels to explain your decisions.

### ICT ACTIVITY

Present your information in the form of a booklet, poster or PowerPoint presentation.

▲ **Figure 17  River Avon, Salisbury (River Restoration Centre)**

Locate a stretch of river near to your home or school that you think could be improved. Take photographs to show the main features of the river and its environment. Identify some of the problems and issues that you think need addressing.

Suggest ways in which you think the river and its environment could be improved both for wildlife (plants, birds, fish, insects, etc.) and for people. Use sketches and maps to help you re-design the area.

# People

**In this chapter you will study:**

- the geography of names
- discovering your geographical roots
- population growth in the UK
- population patterns in the UK
- people on the move
- immigration to the UK.

# A What's in a name?

Do you know that in 2006 the most popular girls' names were Jessica, Olivia and Grace? The most popular boys names were Jack, Thomas and Joshua. How many people in your class have these names?

Amongst some of the more unusual names given to babies in 2006 were the girls' names Summer and Autumn (there were no Winters or Springs!). Some of the more unusual celebrity names popular with boys were Cruz (son of Victoria and David Beckham) and Maddox (adopted son of Angelina Jolie).

Names can give useful clues about where people have come from. The surnames Jones and Evans, for example, are traditional Welsh names. Names starting with 'Mac' or 'Mc' (such as MacKenzie) tend to have Scottish or Irish origins.

Some people in the UK have their origins elsewhere in the world. Names like Patel suggest an Indian background; whereas Mohammad suggests Pakistani or Middle Eastern. Names like Wong, Yeung and Lai are associated with Hong Kong or China.

Names can also be used to suggest what jobs people have done in the past. The name Mason suggests a stonemason, who is skilled at sculpting stone, Carpenter suggests a link with woodworking, and the name Baker suggests bread making. Can you think of any others?

Names provide important family links with the past. Middle names often relate to parents' or grandparents' names. Occasionally, somewhat unusual 'family' names may be passed on down from one generation to the next.

▲ Figure 1   A group of school children with different names and different backgrounds

## Activity

1 Try to discover some interesting things about your name or the names of some of your family members.
- Why were you given your name(s)?
- Does your surname suggest any place of origin or type of work?
- Are there any family names being passed down through the generations?

Discuss the results of your investigation in class.

# B  Enquiry: Discovering my geographical roots

Do you know what a family tree is? It is a diagram that traces a person's family history back in time through the generations. As it expands to show parents, grandparents, aunts and uncles, so it looks a bit like the branches of a tree (see Figure 2). Connecting with the past gives us a sense of who we are and where we have come from. Some very interesting geographical patterns emerge.

Look at Figure 2. It shows Jeff's family tree. Notice that it is possible to add all sorts of information about each person. When they were born and when they died, where they lived, what job they did and so on. The locations of where the family live can be plotted on a map (see Figure 3). Patterns of migration can also be shown (see Figure 4).

> ## Activity
>
> 2  Carry out an enquiry into your own family tree. Ask relatives to help you construct a family tree (like the one in Figure 2). Draw a map to show the geographical patterns of your family.

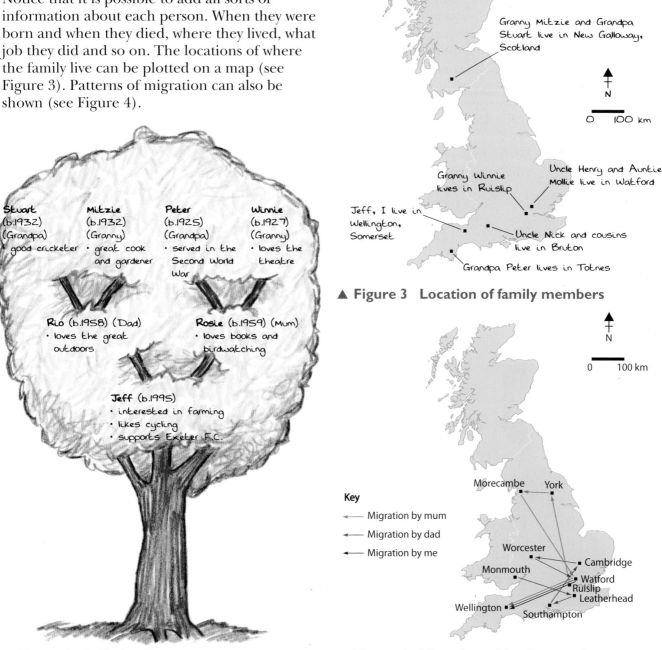

▲ **Figure 3  Location of family members**

▲ **Figure 2  Jeff's family tree**

▲ **Figure 4  Migration of family members**

# C How many people live in the UK?

Every ten years since 1801 (apart from in 1941 due to the Second World War), there has been a national survey of population. This survey is called a **census**. At the last census, in 2001, the total population of the UK was 58,789,194. In 2005 the UK's population reached 60 million. The population for each country in the UK is listed in Figure 5. The next census will be in 2011.

Look at Figure 6. It shows the growth of the UK's population since the Roman invasion in AD43. Notice that the population of the UK remained low and steady for hundreds of years. This was because many people died from illness and disease due to poor living conditions, dirty water and poor food. When conditions improved in the 1800s, such as improved housing, safe drinking water, better food and clothing, people lived longer and the total population started to rise. Look at Figure 6 to see how the UK's population grew rapidly from 1800.

| Country in UK | Population (mid 2005) | Area size (sq km) | Population density (people per sq km) |
|---|---|---|---|
| England | 50,431,700 | 130,281 | 383 |
| Northern Ireland | 1,724,400 | 13,576 | 125 |
| Scotland | 5,094,800 | 77,925 | 65 |
| Wales | 2,958,6000 | 20,732 | 142 |
| United Kingdom | 60,209,500 | 242,514 | 246 |

*Source: Office for National Statistics; National Assembly for Wales; General Register Office for Scotland; Northern Ireland Statistics and Research Agency*

▲ **Figure 5   UK population (2007)**

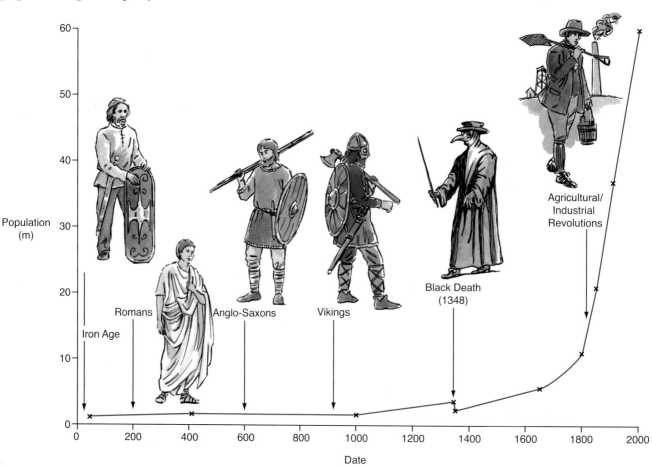

▲ **Figure 6   UK timeline**

## Activities

3  Study Figure 7.

   a)  Use the information in Figure 7 to draw your own timeline like the one in Figure 6. Take time to work out an appropriate horizontal and vertical scale.

   b)  Add the following labels to your graph:

| | |
|---|---|
| ● 200 | Romans in UK |
| ● 600 | Anglo-Saxons in UK |
| ● 920 | Vikings in UK |
| ● 1348 | Black Death |
| ● 1800–1900 | Agricultural/Industrial Revolutions |
| ● 1939–1945 | Second World War. |

   c)  Add some illustrations to your graph (using the internet if you wish).

4  Complete the gaps in the following paragraph (using the graph you drew in Activity 3). Select words and numbers from the list.

When the Romans invaded the UK in AD43, the population was about ___. The population grew only very slowly and actually fell after the Black Death in _____. In 1800, the population had reached ___. It now started to grow very _____ due to improvements in living standards. By _____ the population had reached 37 million. It continued to grow rapidly to reach 60 million in _____ .

1 million  2 million  60 million  slowly  rapidly  carrots  1800  1348  11 million  31 million  32p  1910  reindeer  2005

5  Study the timeline that you drew in Activity 3.

   a)  Use your timeline to suggest when the UK's population will rise to 65 million.

   b)  Can you think why this forecast might turn out to be inaccurate?

| Date | Population (million) |
|---|---|
| AD43 | 1 |
| 400 | 1.5 |
| 1000 | 1.5 |
| 1348 | 3.5 |
| 1350 | 2.25 |
| 1650 | 5.7 |
| 1800 | 11 |
| 1850 | 21 |
| 1910 | 37 |
| 1945 | 49 |
| 2005 | 60 |

▲ **Figure 7   UK population data**          *Source: BBC History*

# D Where do people live in England and Wales?

Look at Figure 9. It is a map that shows the **distribution** (or spread) of population in England and Wales. Look at the key. Notice that the values are 'number of people per hectare'. This is a measure of **population density**.

The map shows that the distribution of people in England and Wales is very uneven. Some places, such as southeast England, the West Midlands and parts of northwest England have a high population density. Other parts of England and Wales, such as large parts of Wales, have much lower population densities.

There are a number of reasons why the population is not evenly spread in England and Wales.

- **Climate:** The harsh climate of Wales with low temperatures, heavy rain and strong winds makes it difficult for people choosing to live and work in these areas (Figure 8). Southeast England has a much warmer and drier climate, which is more attractive for people to live in. Farming is more likely to be successful where the climate does not suffer from extremes.

- **Physical landscape:** It is much easier to build houses and roads on the flat lands of southern England than it is to build on the high steep slopes of North Wales (Figure 8).

- **Trade and transport:** Parts of Wales are quite remote from the main industrial centres of the UK and are a long way from the rest of Europe. Southeast England has the capital city, London (Figure 10) at its heart and it is quick and easy to travel to Europe. Liverpool has been an important port for many centuries and many industries have grown up on Merseyside. The same is true for Newcastle-upon-Tyne.

- **Industry:** Hundreds of years ago industry began to develop on the coalfields in the UK (see Figure 11). Today these areas, such as those in South Wales, northeast England and Yorkshire, are still heavily populated. Other industrial areas such as Manchester and Birmingham have high population densities.

## Activity

6 For this activity you will need to use an atlas and Figure 9.

a) Match the following locations to the letters A to J. Use a colour code to identify whether the location has a high or a low population density:
- Greater London
- Greater Manchester (centred on Manchester)
- North Wales
- South Wales
- Devon and Cornwall
- Birmingham
- Liverpool
- Lake District (northwest England)
- Leeds
- Newcastle-upon-Tyne.

b) Use your atlas to name one other location that has a high population density.

c) Use your atlas to name one other location that has a low population density.

▲ Figure 8  Mountains in Wales: a sparsely populated area

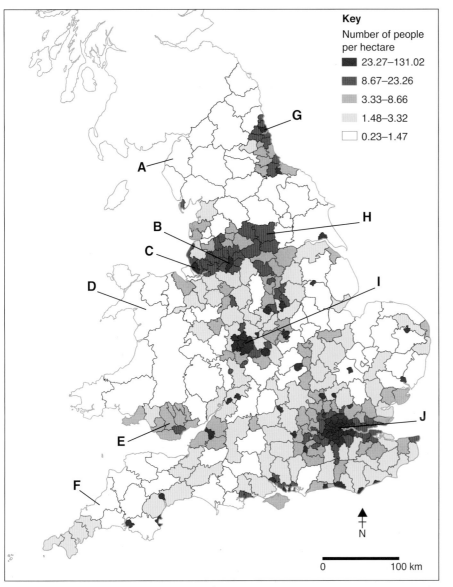

**Key**

Number of people per hectare

- ■ 23.27–131.02
- ■ 8.67–23.26
- ▨ 3.33–8.66
- ░ 1.48–3.32
- □ 0.23–1.47

0          100 km

N

▲ **Figure 9   Map of population density in England and Wales**

## Activity

7  Use the map in Figure 9 to discover more about the distribution of population in your home region.

a)  Make a copy of the distribution of population in your home region (or trace a section from the map in Figure 9). Be sure to include a key. Use an atlas to label the main towns, roads and upland areas. Label any other features that you think might help to account for variations in population density.

b)  Use an atlas (together with other resources provided by your teacher) to suggest reasons for the areas of high density and the areas of low density. You may find useful additional information in your school resource centre or on the internet.

▲ **Figure 10   Oblique aerial view of London**

▲ **Figure 11   Historic view of coalfields in Derbyshire**

# E People on the move

As we have discovered from our study of names, people move about from place to place. This is called **migration**. The photographs in Figure 12 illustrate some examples of migration in the UK.

Some migrations involve moving thousands of miles from one continent to another. This would include people who have moved to the UK from Africa, Asia or the Caribbean. Remember, too, that birds and other animals migrate over massive distances, such as swallows (see Figure 13) and whales. Other forms of migration can also be very local and short-term, such as going to work or going on holiday to a nearby coastline.

One of the most frequent short-term migrations is the daily journey from home to work. Each morning and evening the roads become busy and trains and buses are filled with people travelling to and from work or school (Figure 14). These busy times of day are called the **rush hour**.

▲ Figure 13 Swallows

▲ Figure 12 Different forms of migration

# Activities

8  Study Figure 12.

a) Look closely at each photograph in Figure 12. Work with your neighbour to discuss what you think is happening in each photograph. Suggest which migrations are short term (few days or weeks) and which are long term (months or years).

b) Apart from your journeys between home and school, list some recent migrations involving you and your family (e.g. holidays).

c) In the summer, lots of people travel to the coast for their holidays. Suggest some problems that this mass migration can cause in coastal areas.

d) One of the photographs in Figure 12 shows people moving house. Make a list of some of the reasons why people decide to move house.

9  Study Figure 13. Can you think of any wildlife migrations apart from swallows and whales?

10  Study Figure 14.

a) Describe what is happening in the photograph.

b) Why do you think this time of day is called the 'rush hour'?

c) Suggest some problems caused by the daily migration to work.

11  A class of Year 7 pupils was asked to record some details about their journey to school. They were asked to record the method of transport (car, walk, bicycle, etc.), the average time taken to get to school in the morning, and the distance of the journey. The information was presented in the form of a **scattergraph** (Figure 15). The trend is made clearer by the drawing of a **best fit line**, which roughly splits the points in half. Study the scattergraph and answer the following questions.

a) Which pupil has the longest journey to school?

b) Which pupil spends the longest time travelling to school?

c) How many pupils walk to school?

d) How long does it take James to travel to school?

e) Use the word 'increases' or 'decreases' to complete the following sentence describing the overall trend of the results.

'The scattergraph shows that as distance increases, travel time …'

f) Notice on the graph that one or two points are quite a long way away from the best fit line. These are called **anomalies.**

● Can you suggest possible reasons why Daisy's journey to school takes longer than would be expected?

● Why do you think Jack's journey is much quicker compared with others travelling the same distance?

12  Carry out your own class survey of the journey from home to school. Draw a scattergraph similar to Figure 15. Attempt to plot a best fit line. Describe the pattern shown on your graph. Try to explain any anomalies.

▲ Figure 14   The rush hour

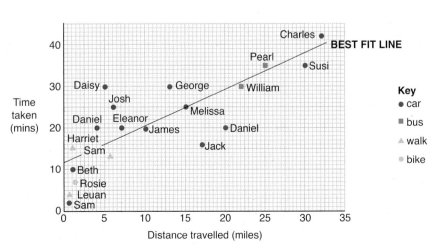

▲ Figure 15   Scattergraph showing Y7 pupils' journeys to school

# F Emigration and immigration

Every year some 100,000 people decide to move away from the UK to live abroad. When people move out of their own country to another it is called **emigration**. In 2006 a survey discovered that 5.5 million people born in the UK now live abroad. The majority of 'expats' (as they are called) have chosen to live in Australia, Spain and the USA.

Most emigrants are young and skilled workers. They are mostly moving in search of employment. Some move to be near relatives, or to find a warm and sunny place to retire. Moving to another country is not as easy as it sounds. There is a huge amount of paperwork to be done and local people are not always welcoming. Sometimes people decide to move back to the UK when things don't turn out as they had expected. Read the emigration stories showing different experiences (Figure 16).

People who decide to move to a different country are called **immigrants**. The UK has a long traditional of **immigration** and prides itself on being multicultural and multiracial. Look around you in any town centre and you will see people from all parts of the world (Figure 17).

▲ **Figure 17 Multicultural UK**

In the 1960s, large numbers of people came to the UK from the Caribbean, India and Pakistan. They came seeking a better life from relatively poor parts of the world. More recently, people have come to the UK from other parts of Europe, for example Poland. Many work on farms (Figure 18), in hotels or in the building trade. Often they stay just for a few years to make some money before returning home to their families.

## Blog

I will be leaving UK shores for a life in Miami very soon. The people are very friendly and my accent attracts attention everywhere I go. Things are so cheap there. I have a wardrobe packed with the same grey slacks and it cost me next to nothing.

**Sam, Hull, Yorkshire**

I went to work in Florida, USA after quitting my job in 1999. I worked in the tourist industry in a hotel and it was hell. Low pay, no time off and long days – the weather was lovely, but if you are working you may as well be in an office in London. I missed cups of tea and fish and chips! I now work in London.

**Rebecca, Reading, Surrey**

▲ **Figure 16 Emigration stories**

▲ Figure 18   Workers on land picking fruit or vegetables

## Activities

13 Study Figure 16.

a) What is the difference between an emigrant and an immigrant?

b) Suggest two reasons why Bobby wanted to move to Florida.

c) Can you think of another reason why people from the UK might be attracted to emigrate to the USA? *who?*

d) Why has Luke decided to return to London having emigrated to Miami?

e) If you had a free choice, where in the world would you emigrate to and why?

f) What do you think you might miss from living in the UK if you and your family emigrated?

14 Study Figure 18.

a) Describe what the workers are doing in the photograph.

b) Why do you think this type of work needs so many people?

c) Suggest some of the hardships faced by the workers doing this work.

## G   Issue: Should immigration to the UK be allowed to continue?

Immigration is a controversial issue in the UK. It is estimated that two-thirds of the current population growth of the UK is due to immigration. About 7.5 per cent of the UK's population were born abroad. Should the UK government continue to let people enter the country to live and work?

### Why do people move to the UK?

People move to the UK for a variety of reasons. Most people come because of work. Some come as students. Some come seeking refuge from wars or natural disasters and others come through marriage. Look at the accounts in Figure 19.

Immigrants come from a variety of different countries (Figure 20). The majority have come from Asia, particularly India and Pakistan. In recent years many have migrated from the poorer European Union countries (such as Poland).

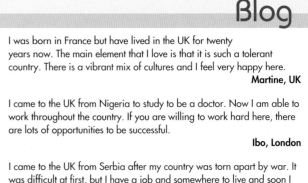

## Blog

I was born in France but have lived in the UK for twenty years now. The main element that I love is that it is such a tolerant country. There is a vibrant mix of cultures and I feel very happy here.

**Martine, UK**

I came to the UK from Nigeria to study to be a doctor. Now I am able to work throughout the country. If you are willing to work hard here, there are lots of opportunities to be successful.

**Ibo, London**

I came to the UK from Serbia after my country was torn apart by war. It was difficult at first, but I have a job and somewhere to live and soon I will be applying for citizenship. There is a lot of negative commentary on immigration in the UK, but a lot of people don't see the positives – now I feel safe and happy, but also I am contributing to the economy.

**Adrijana, Manchester**

I joined my English husband in the UK five years ago. I live in Devon and it's a beautiful part of the country – I wouldn't want to be anywhere else! Everyone has been very welcoming here and I'm getting used to British food. But there is a Polish supermarket down the road if I do miss my mum's cooking!

**Iwona, Devon**

▲ Figure 19   Personal accounts of reasons for moving to the UK

## What kind of life do immigrants have in the UK?

Most immigrants enjoy a better quality of life in the UK than they would have done if they had stayed at home (Figure 21). However, a number of immigrants have to suffer low wages and poor working conditions. Some become involved in crime and prostitution as they try to earn enough money to survive.

## What are the advantages and disadvantages of immigration?

Immigrants are often willing and very hard working. They are prepared to take low paid jobs that British people do not want. In this way, they have helped the UK to continue its economic growth in recent years. Immigrants can add a great deal to the cultural life of the UK, bringing fresh ideas and introducing fashions, music and foods.

However, some people believe that the flow of immigrants to the UK is causing problems. They are increasing the pressure on housing and health care. By accepting low pay, they are keeping pay levels low for everybody else. Sometimes there is unrest between the different communities.

| | | | |
|---|---|---|---|
| Republic of Ireland | 494,850 | USA | 155,030 |
| India | 466,416 | Bangladesh | 154,201 |
| Pakistan | 320,767 | South Africa | 140,201 |
| Germany | 262,276 | Kenya | 129,356 |
| Caribbean | 254,740 | Italy | 107,002 |

Source: BBC News

▲ **Figure 20   Top ten non-UK birth countries**

## Activities

15  Draw up a table to show the advantages and disadvantages of immigration in the UK. Use the information in this section, together with additional information from the internet using the website links.

16  Do you think immigration to the UK should be allowed to continue or should it be stopped? Write a few sentences describing your own immigration policy. Consider under what circumstances people should be allowed to move into the UK.

# Jerry Adesanmi: a story of immigration

Jerry Adesanmi was born in Nigeria in 1959. In 1988, following the example of his brother, he came to the UK to study. Jerry originally planned to return home after graduating, but two years after his arrival his family joined him and he has been living in the UK ever since.

As Nigeria is a former British colony Jerry speaks good English and feels safe living in the UK, compared with Nigeria, which has problems with law and order. He now works in IT support and also has a part-time job as a cleaning supervisor. In this role he oversees a workforce of immigrants, mainly from Africa and Brazil (see photo).

Although Jerry enjoys living in the UK he plans to return to Nigeria when he retires. After all, says Jerry, 'Home is home'.

▲ **Figure 21   The life of a Nigerian immigrant in the UK – Jerry Adesanmi (centre of photo) with Brazilian staff members**

## ICT ACTIVITY

Imagine that you are a young migrant from Brazil. You and your best friend have just finished university and you have decided to travel to the UK to earn some money. You plan to stay for several months, maybe a year.

Use the internet or a local newspaper to try to find the following.

- A place to live in your local town. It needs to be a rented property. Try to find the best deal for the lowest price. You do not have much money.

- A short-term job, for example on a farm, as a cleaner or in a local factory. (Try to find a well-paid job!)

- You are keen to become part of the local community. What sort of things could you do to become accepted?

- Do you think you will be happy here? Explain your answer.

# Settlement

## CHAPTER 7

**In this chapter you will study:**

- settlement site – why settlements were built where they were
- local fieldwork opportunities in villages
- changing land uses
- OS mapwork
- green towns and cities
- managing transport.

# A   Settlement site

Have you ever wondered why your town or village grew up where it did? Why did the first settlers decide to build their houses on this plot of land and not somewhere else?

The land on which a settlement is built is called the settlement **site**. There are many reasons affecting the choice of site:

- **Defence:** Is the site safe? Can it be defended? Hilltops are good defensive positions (Figure 1). Land surrounded by water can also be easily defended. However, a settlement too close to a river might be in danger of flooding!

- **Food supply:** Land close by that is suitable for growing crops or raising animals is important. Flat, fertile land is found close to rivers.

- **Water:** Fresh drinking water is essential. This explains why so many old settlements were sited near wells or springs, or by rivers and lakes (Figure 2).

- **Wood:** Trees are very useful for building and also for fuel. Many early settlements were sited near to woods or forests.

- **Roads:** Places where roads or paths joined were popular early settlement sites (Figure 3). A crossroads would have plenty of people passing through and would be an ideal site for inns and shops.

Can you think of any other factors that might affect settlement sites?

▲ **Figure 2   Village well**

▲ **Figure 1   Conisbrough**

▲ **Figure 3   Village crossroads**

## Activities

1 Study Figures 1, 2 and 3.

a) For each photograph suggest reasons for the settlement site.

b) Not all hilltop sites turn out to be quite as good as expected. Can you think of some possible problems of siting a settlement on the top of a hill?

2 Study Figure 5. Imagine that you are part of a group of travelling people in search of somewhere to settle and build homes.

a) Describe the scene. Write a few sentences to describe your first impressions of the area.

b) Four possible sites (A to D) have been identified by your leader. Make a copy of the table in Figure 4. Working in pairs or small groups, discuss the advantages and disadvantages of each site. Record your thoughts in the table.

c) Now discuss within your group which site you think is best and why.

d) Conduct a class discussion with each group reporting its findings. Try to agree on the best site within your class.

| Site | Advantages | Disadvantages |
|------|-----------|---------------|
| A | | |
| B | | |
| C | | |
| D | | |

▲ Figure 4  Advantages and disadvantages of settlement sites

▲ Figure 5  Possible settlement sites

## Local Fieldwork

# Village study

**Look at Figure 6. It is a sketch map of the village of Trull on the outskirts of Taunton in Somerset. The map was completed following fieldwork by a group of Year 7 pupils.**

The map shows some of the main characteristics of Trull. It shows the location of the shops, the church and the primary school. Other information has also been added, such as the location of bus stops.

Carry out a similar study of a village near to your home or school. Aim to produce a report on your village including a detailed sketch map, some labelled photographs and some writing.

On a base map of the village, locate and label as many features as you can. (Use Figure 6 to give you some ideas.)

Consider the following questions as you walk around your village.

- Are there any signs that the village is growing? Is there evidence of new buildings?

- Does the village appear to be in decline? Have shops closed down? Are there lots of houses for sale?

- Is the village well served by public transport? (Look for bus stops and bus timetables.)

- Does the village seem to be popular? Are there lots of people in the village?

- What are the public spaces like? Are grassy areas well looked after? Are there colourful flowerbeds? Is there a children's playground and is it in good condition?

- Do you think the village is a nice place to live?

Take some photographs of your village (but think carefully about what you are trying to show). Remember that all photos should be labelled.

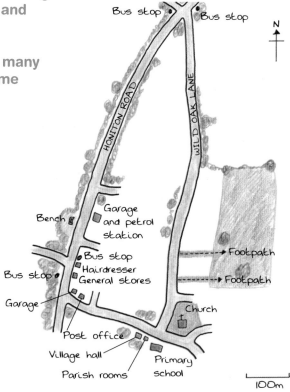

▲ **Figure 6  Completed sketch map of Trull**

# OS map study of New Galloway maps

Study the map folded out from the back of the book (1:50,000 map)

1   Locate New Galloway in grid square 6377.
    a) What are the numbers of the two roads that form the crossroads in the centre of New Galloway?
    b) How might the crossroads help to explain why New Galloway was sited here?
    c) Why do you think New Galloway does not occupy the flat ground next to the Water of Ken?
    d) Most of the woodland on the map is less than 50 years old. However, this environment is clearly well suited to growing trees. In the past, there would have been large areas of natural woodland. Why would this have been an important factor in affecting the choice of site for New Galloway?

2   Locate Kenmure Castle in grid square 6376.
    a) Describe the site of the castle.
    b) Suggest why this site was chosen for the castle.

3   Locate St John's Town of Dalry in grid square 6281. Using evidence from the map, suggest possible reasons why the settlement was sited here.

Study the map folded out from the front of the book (1:25,000 map).

4   Locate New Galloway on the map.
    a) Look closely at the map and make a list of the services (e.g. hotels) in New Galloway in addition to housing.
    b) Do you think New Galloway is a village or a town? Why?

5   Now locate St John's Town of Dalry.
    a) What additional services can you see that are not in New Galloway?
    b) Do you think as the name of the settlement suggests that it really is a town? Explain your answer.
    c) Before water was piped into St John's Town of Dalry, where do you think people got their fresh water?
    d) Do you think St John's Town of Dalry is at risk from flooding? Explain your answer.
    e) A developer wants to build houses on the Holm of Dalry. Suggest some advantages and disadvantages of this site for a new housing development.

6   Study the map in the front of the book (1:25,000 map). The local planning authority has decided to build a new Visitor Centre in the area. Where do you think the new Visitor Centre should be sited and why?

# B  Changing land use in towns and cities

The land use in towns and cities is constantly changing. In many city centres older industrial areas have been demolished and replaced with gleaming office blocks and shopping centres on the outskirts, retail and leisure parks have been built. Can you think of some changes of land use that have taken place in your local town or city?

## The 2012 Olympic and Paralympic Games

The most recent focus for change in London is in Stratford, just a few miles north of London Docklands and Canary Wharf. This is the site of the 2012 Olympic and Paralympics Games.

The site has the advantage of mainline, Underground and international rail links.

Stratford is one of the poorest parts of the capital. The Olympics will provide a much-needed boost to the local **economy** and it is expected to improve the environment too. It is hoped that the Olympics will trigger further improvements in the area and that there will be many benefits now, and in the future, for the local residents.

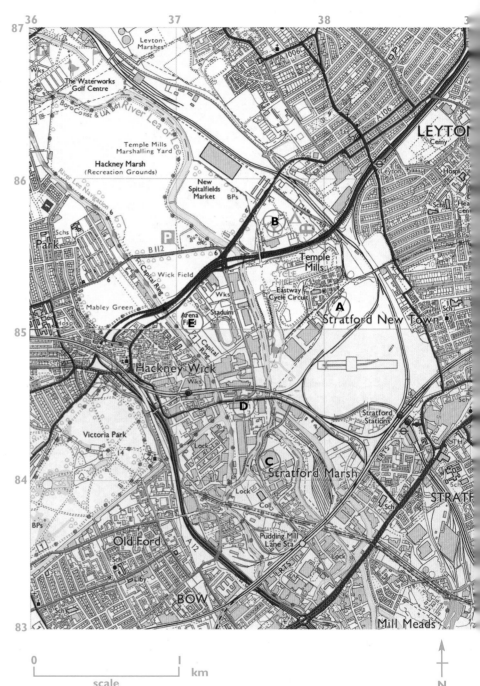

▲ **Figure 7   OS 1:25,000 map extract of Stratford site**

# Activities

3  Study Figures 7 and 8. Write down three reasons why Stratford is a good site for the Olympics.

For the rest of these activities, you can access the Olympics plan from the website **www.london2012.com**. Click on 'News', then Images' and then 'Maps', where you can download this image and explore it in more detail.

4  Study Figures 7 and 8. Take time to locate the planned developments on the OS map. The easiest way to do this is to look at the main road network that encircles the bulk of the Olympic site.

   a) Use a ruler to measure the straight-line distance across the Olympic site from the Stratford bus station at 387844 to the 'place of worship with a tower' in Hackney Wick at 367848. Give your answer to the nearest whole kilometre.

   b) Apart from railway lines and industrial buildings, there are lots of waterways crossing the Olympic site. What is the name of the main river that flows through the centre of the site from north to south?

   c) Look at Figure 8. How are these waterways going to be used to make the Olympic site attractive?

   d) Do you think it is a good idea to use the waterways in this way or should they be piped underground and hidden from view?

   e) How is the land at locations **A** to **E** on Figure 7 going to be used during the Olympics?

   f) Look closely at Figure 8. How are people expected to travel to the Olympic site?

5  The Olympics are expected to improve the quality of life for local people.

   a) Work in pairs to suggest some of the benefits that the Olympics might bring to the area.

   b) Why do you think some local people did not want the Olympics to be located here?

   c) If you lived nearby, how would you feel about the area being developed for the Olympics?

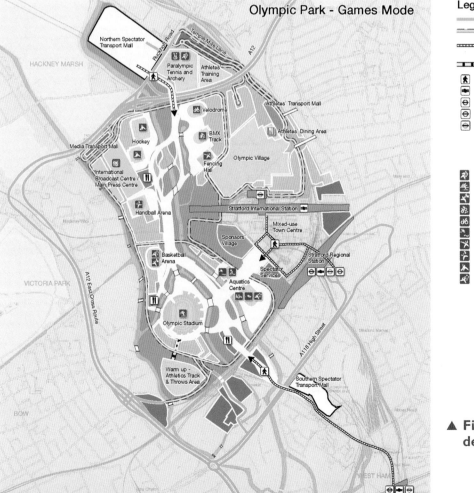

▲ Figure 8  Olympics plan for developments of the site

## C  Green towns and cities

In the past, as towns and cities grew ever larger, there was little concern about the need to provide people with green spaces and parks. Every piece of land was used for roads, pavements, shopping centres or housing estates. It was seen as a waste to leave areas green and undeveloped.

Nowadays, planners understand the need to bring a flavour of the countryside into towns and cities. Green areas and trees provide pleasant places for people to sit and read (Figure 9). They provide natural habitats for birds and animals. The flowers and trees add colour to an otherwise drab environment. Green areas absorb rainwater that would otherwise flow over the roads and pavements, possibly causing flooding.

Look at Figure 10. It shows a small part of central London between the British Museum and Kings Cross Station. Notice that there are many small green areas, often forming squares between the roads. One particularly interesting green area is Camley Street Nature Park in square G1. Created on industrial waste ground it is a haven for wildlife (Figure 11) in an otherwise fairly gloomy area close to St Pancras Station. Children from nearby schools and local residents are frequent visitors to the park and it is carefully maintained to be as natural as possible.

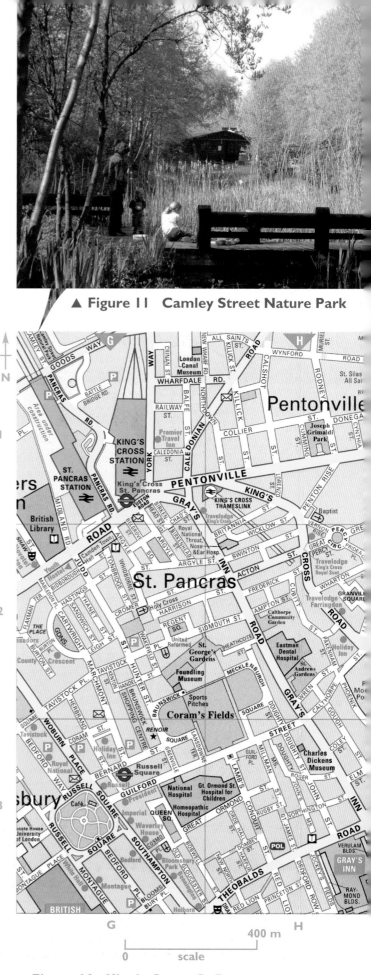

▲ **Figure 11   Camley Street Nature Park**

▲ **Figure 10   King's Cross, St Pancras**

▲ **Figure 9   Green space in Liverpool**

## Activities

6 Study Figure 9.

   **a)** Why do you think this green space is popular with local people?

   **b)** How do you think this green space changes during the course of a year?

   **c)** Can you suggest anything that could be done to improve the area still further?

   **d)** Imagine that a local developer wants to build on this green space. Write a short letter to the local newspaper suggesting why the area should not be developed.

7 Study Figure 11.

   **a)** Describe the scene in the photograph.

   **b)** Is there any evidence that this green space is in the middle of a major city?

   **c)** Do you think it is good to have nature parks such as Camley Street Nature Park in towns and cities? Give reasons for your answer.

8 Study Figure 10.

   **a)** Locate Russell Square in grid square G3. Describe the pattern of paths.

   **b)** Why do you think the paths were designed in this way?

   **c)** What is the building in the park used for?

   **d)** Now locate Coram's Fields in the centre of Figure 10. What is one of the uses of this green space?

   **e)** Give the name and grid square of one other green space in Figure 10.

9 Imagine that you could create a new green space on Figure 10.

   **a)** Where would you locate the green space and why?

   **b)** How should your green space be used by local people and why?

   **c)** Draw an enlarged sketch map to show the location of your green space. Add any design features such as paths, benches and cafés. Don't forget to give your green space a name.

## LOCAL FIELDWORK

An interesting development in recent years is the creation of 'green maps'. These are maps that plot the location of green and sustainable aspects of towns and cities, such as parks, recycling centres and areas of artistic interest. Local communities research and draw them.

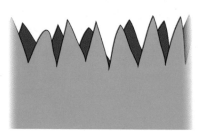

- Look up the Green Maps website at http://www.greenmap.org/greenhouse to find out more.

- Produce a Green map for the area close to your school. To do this you will need a base map of your local area and a copy of the standard Green Map symbols (available on the website). Take great care when outside.

- Divide up the survey area to enable the class to work in small groups. Carry out the mapping by plotting the correct symbols onto your base map.

- When each group has completed the mapping, the information can be combined for the whole class.

- A final neat version can then be drawn and used for display in your school. It might be nice to publicise your Green Map on the school's website, or in a newsletter to parents.

## D  Issue: How can traffic be managed in towns and cities?

Every day in the UK, millions of people travel into and out of towns and cities to go to work, school or to the shops. As car ownership has increased, so more people choose to drive. This has created many problems (see Figure 12).

To reduce the problems, and help traffic and people move more smoothly, a variety of transport management schemes have been introduced (Figure 14).

### Managing transport in Droitwich Spa

Droitwich Spa is a small town six miles northeast of Worcester. It is a very ancient town dating back to before Roman times. The growth of Droitwich was due to local salt deposits, which have been extracted for hundreds of years. In the nineteenth century, the health-giving powers of bathing in salt led to Droitwich becoming a **spa town**. It grew rapidly from then on.

Traffic in Droitwich has been a big issue because the historic centre with its old buildings (Figure 13) and narrow streets is not well suited to large volumes of traffic.

▲ **Figure 13  Droitwich centre**

| Traffic Management | | Description |
|---|---|---|
| Park and ride | | Cars are parked on the outskirts of the town or city and frequent buses transport people into the centre. |
| Bus/car sharing lanes | | Road lanes where only certain users are allowed. Traffic here flows faster than in the normal lanes, encouraging people to travel by bus or car share. |
| Congestion charging | | Some cities charge cars and other private vehicles if they enter the centre. In 2007, the daily charge in London was £8. Use the internet to find out what it is now. |
| Mass transit systems | | Apart from buses, some cities have underground trains and even trams. |
| Cycleways | | People are encouraged to cycle and many towns and cities have cycleways to help them to do so safely. |

▲ **Figure 14  Examples of traffic management options**

▲ **Figure 12  Inner-city traffic congestion**

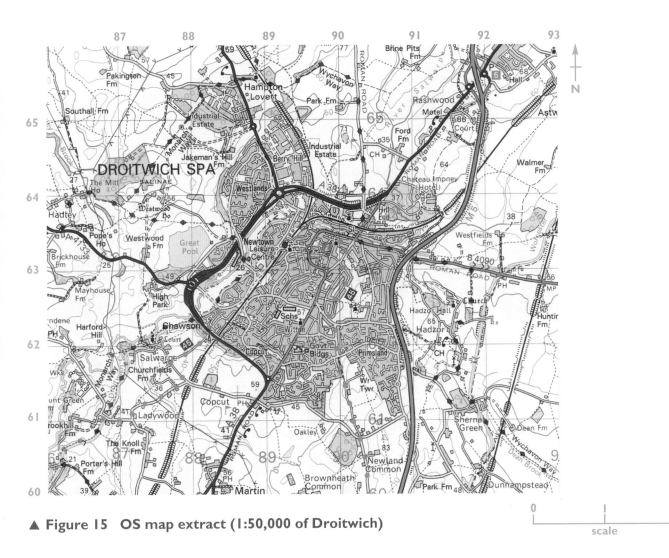

▲ Figure 15   OS map extract (1:50,000 of Droitwich)

0        1        2
|_____|_____| km
scale

## Activity

10   Look at Figure 15. Notice that there is a major by-pass to the west of Droitwich that keeps through-traffic out of the town centre. Can you see where the old A38 would have been, running straight through the middle of the town? Although some people travel in to Droitwich by train, the vast majority use cars.

  The aim of this Activity is for you to work in small groups to identify a suitable site for a Park and Ride Scheme in Droitwich. To do this you should work through the following steps:

a)   Consider and discuss the site requirements for a Park and Ride Scheme. You can't just site it anywhere! You will need about a quarter of a grid square of land for the car parking. Think about ease of access by cars. How easy is it to get into the town centre?

b)   Now look around the edge of Droitwich identifying a number of possible sites. Try to agree a 'shortlist' of three best sites.

c)   Draw up a table to record advantages and disadvantages of each of your shortlisted sites.

d)   Discuss and agree on the best site.

e)   Draw a sketch map to show the location of the site and use annotations to describe its advantages.

f)   Compare your choice of site with other groups in your class.

# LOCAL FIELDWORK

Carry out a study of transport management in your local area, town or city. Use base maps to plot the different forms of transport management in operation. Make use of digital photographs too. The following list will help get you started.

- Are there any 'bus only' lanes?
- Where are 'no parking' double yellow lines?
- Is there a one-way system in the middle of town?
- Is there a by-pass to keep through-traffic out of the centre?
- Are people encouraged to 'car share'?
- Is there a congestion charge?
- Is there a Park and Ride scheme?
- Where are the car parks?

Is there a problem with traffic in your town? To find out, you may need to do some research involving a questionnaire of local people. You could look up articles in the local press.

Suggest ways of reducing the problems you have identified. Consider the various options outlined in this section and make your suggestions backed up with sound reasons.

# Farming and Industry

## CHAPTER 8

**In this chapter you will study:**

- the world of work and the different sectors of the economy
- a mixed farm in Scotland
- the process of making and selling ice cream
- ways of making money on farms without farming.

# A   The world of work

Most people in the UK get a job when they leave school or university. They get paid for the work that they do. The money that they earn is used to pay for their living costs, such as rent for their home, food, transport, and to support their interests and hobbies.

Some of the money that people earn goes to the government in taxes. This is used for the benefit of the whole country, such as for funding the National Health Service. The word **economic** is used to describe the buying and selling of goods and services.

There are many different types of work that people do and it is possible to sort them into three groups or sectors.

**Primary sector** – these are jobs that involve extracting natural materials from the land or the oceans. Farming, fishing and mining are all good examples of primary jobs.

**Secondary (manufacturing) sector** – these jobs involve making items or products from raw materials. Good examples include making cars, food products and clothes. People involved in this sector often work in factories.

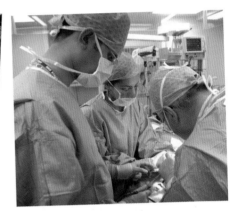

**Tertiary sector** – most people in the UK work in this sector of the economy. These are jobs to do with services and administration. People who work in call centres, teachers, doctors, cleaners and solicitors are all part of the tertiary sector.

▲ **Figure 1   Trawler fisherman**   ▲ **Figure 2   Clothes factory**   ▲ **Figure 3   Doctors in a hospital**

**SECOND CHEFS**

Required for busy kitchen, carvery à la carte, bar menus and special boards to include weekends.
**Min 30hrs p/w experience preferred.**

Please call Bob Smith or Gail Wren on 555 6297

**TRAINEE DENTAL NURSE REQUIRED**

Full inhouse training given to run alongside a national certificate course. Please apply by email attaching CV to D.Smithson@dental.gov.uk

**URGENTLY REQUIRED**
**THREE BUS / COACH DRIVERS**
**PART-TIME**

Good rates of pay
(must be over 25 for insurance)

Please contact Ken Cook on 555 7216
(between the hours of 9am and 5pm only)

**ASSEMBLERS/ TESTERS**

Wanted for engineering company. £6.50 ph. Training given to the right candidates. Own transport useful, but not essential.

email First@Employment.Ltd

**FARM WORK**
Part-time help needed with apple harvest.
Ring Steve 555 4111

**SALES ADVISOR**

Working for a local car showroom. Previous sales experience and knowledge of cars would be advantage. Salary and commission.

Please contact Rachel@Activejobs.com

**EXPERIENCED PATTERN CUTTER**

For young fashion clothing manufacturer. Must be able to interpret designers' concepts into original first patterns. Good working conditions. Please call for interview 555 1798

## Activity

1   Study Figure 4. It is a collection of local newspaper adverts for jobs.

   a)   Work in pairs to sort the adverts into primary, secondary and tertiary. Present your answers in the form of a table.

   b)   Add three more jobs for each sector to your table.

▲ **Figure 4   Selection of local newspaper adverts for jobs**

## B   Mackie's of Scotland

Next time you go to a supermarket, have a look at the ice cream in the freezer section. See if you can find any ice cream made by Mackie's of Scotland. Mackie's ice cream (Figure 5) is a well-known and very popular 'luxury' ice cream made on a family farm in Aberdeenshire. Ice cream production started on the farm in 1986.

Mackie's of Scotland employs about 70 people. Some people work on the farm looking after the cows and growing crops. These people are employed in the **primary** sector. Some work in the ice cream parlour making the ice cream. These people work in the **secondary** sector. Other people work in sales, marketing and advertising. They promote and sell the ice cream all over the world. These are **tertiary** sector jobs.

In the rest of this chapter, you will find out more about what happens on the farm and learn how the milk and cream produced by the cows is made into Mackie's luxury ice cream.

▲ **Figure 5   Mackie's ice cream**

## C Westertown Farm: a Scottish mixed farm

Mackie's ice cream is made at Westertown Farm, some 30 km northwest of Aberdeen in Scotland (Figure 6). It is a large farm covering 650 hectares. (To understand how large this is, one hectare is roughly the size of a football pitch.) Much of the work on the farm involves caring for the 500 dairy cattle that produce the milk for the ice cream. The farm currently employs thirteen people.

▲ **Figure 6 Map showing location of Westertown Farm in Aberdeenshire**

Look at the photograph in Figure 7, which shows part of Westertown Farm. Notice that most of the land is grassland. This is called **pasture** and it is used by the cattle for grazing. The gently rolling landscape is well suited for growing grass and for keeping animals. There is enough rainfall in this part of Scotland to help the grass grow well. Some grass is cut and used as **hay** (dried grass) or **silage** (fermented grass) to feed the cattle in the winter when the outside pasture is unsuitable. Elsewhere on the farm, land is used for growing cereals, such as wheat and barley. Wheat is used to make flour for bread. Barley is used in brewing and also as cattle food. Potatoes are also grown on the farm. You can see why Westertown Farm is an example of a **mixed farm**!

Twice a day the cows are taken to the milking parlour to be milked (Figure 8). Each cow produces about 20 litres of milk a day, which is equivalent to about 2.5 litres of double cream. To produce this amount of cream, each cow eats 35 kg of food a day and deposits 50 litres of muck! Some of the animal waste (the muck) is sprayed onto fields as a natural free fertiliser to help the grass grow.

The cows are well looked after, as an unhappy cow does not produce any milk. Each cow has its own lying space complete with mattress. They have feed available at all times with fresh food added twice a day. A vet comes on a routine visit once a week and any sick animals are moved to a hospital area.

In common with many farms nowadays, the farmer at Westertown Farm is concerned to look after the environment. Fifty hectares (think of an area covered by approximately 50 football pitches) of trees have been planted around the farm (Figure 10). These areas have been designed to provide habitats for wildlife. Grass strips have been sown around some of the fields to create 'wildlife corridors' to link the areas of woodland together. There are wetland areas and a pond to encourage a variety of wildlife.

▲ **Figure 7 Mackie's farm**

▲ Figure 8   Cows in cattleshed

▲ Figure 9   Planting seeds

▲ Figure 10   Newly-planted trees

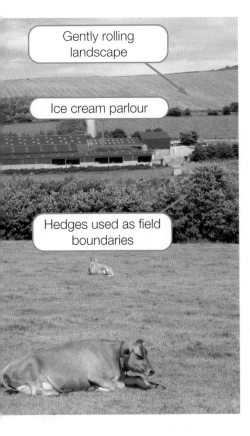

Gently rolling landscape

Ice cream parlour

Hedges used as field boundaries

## Activities

2  The workings of a farm can be shown in the form of a diagram called a **farm system**. The **inputs** (such as the climate and the quality of the land) affect what the farmer does. The **processes** are the jobs that a farmer does on the farm. These are 'doing' activities (and usually end with the letters ' . . .ing'), such as ploughing and harvesting. The **outputs** are what a farmer produces (such as eggs or potatoes).

a)  On a blank sheet of A4 paper, write the three headings 'Inputs', 'Processes' and 'Outputs' across the top of the paper (as in Figure 11, page 100).

b)  The boxes in Figure 11 are muddled up. Match them with the correct headings, and copy them on to your diagram in the right place. Can you add any other details to your diagram?

c)  Add some colour and simple sketches to make the diagram attractive to look at.

3  Study the information about Westertown Farm and attempt the following questions.

a)  Why is Westertown Farm a mixed farm?

b)  In what way is the climate ideal for growing grass?

c)  How is grass stored for use in the winter?

d)  If one cow produces 50 litres of muck a day, how many litres of muck does the herd of 500 cows produce in a day?

e)  What do you think about each cow having its own mattress?

4  Study Figure 7. Notice that hedges separate the fields.

a)  What are the advantages to the farmer of using hedges?

b)  What are the advantages of hedges to wildlife?

c)  What is a 'wildlife corridor'?

d)  Can you think which animals might make use of a wildlife corridor to move around?

e)  Do you think 'wildlife corridors' are a good idea? Explain your answer.

5  Study Figure 12 on page 100. Mackie's farm is marked on the map as 'Westertown'.

a)  What is the height above sea level of the farm buildings at Westertown Farm in grid square 7631?

b)  Locate the highest point on the farm. Give its height above sea level and six-figure grid reference. What is the name of the hill?

c)  What man-made features have been located on this hill?

d)  Why do you think they have been sited here?

e)  What type of woodland is found at 757318?

f)  There is a lot of woodland on the farm. Why do you think the farmer has decided not to clear it to create more land for farming?

g)  Locate field X. This does not belong to the farm. Imagine that this field is available for sale. Do you think the farmer should buy it? Explain your answer.

h)  You have been asked to suggest a one-way system for lorries at the farm to make access easier. Draw a simple sketch map to show your suggested one-way system.

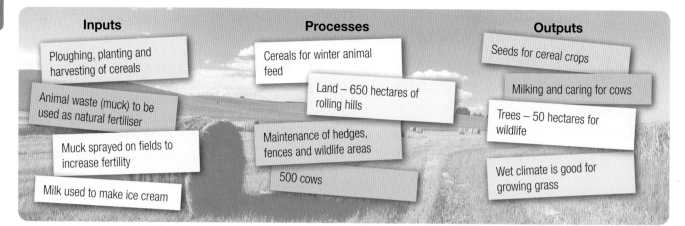

| Inputs | Processes | Outputs |
| --- | --- | --- |
| Ploughing, planting and harvesting of cereals | Cereals for winter animal feed | Seeds for cereal crops |
| Animal waste (muck) to be used as natural fertiliser | Land – 650 hectares of rolling hills | Milking and caring for cows |
| Muck sprayed on fields to increase fertility | Maintenance of hedges, fences and wildlife areas | Trees – 50 hectares for wildlife |
| Milk used to make ice cream | 500 cows | Wet climate is good for growing grass |

▲ **Figure 11 Farm system diagram**

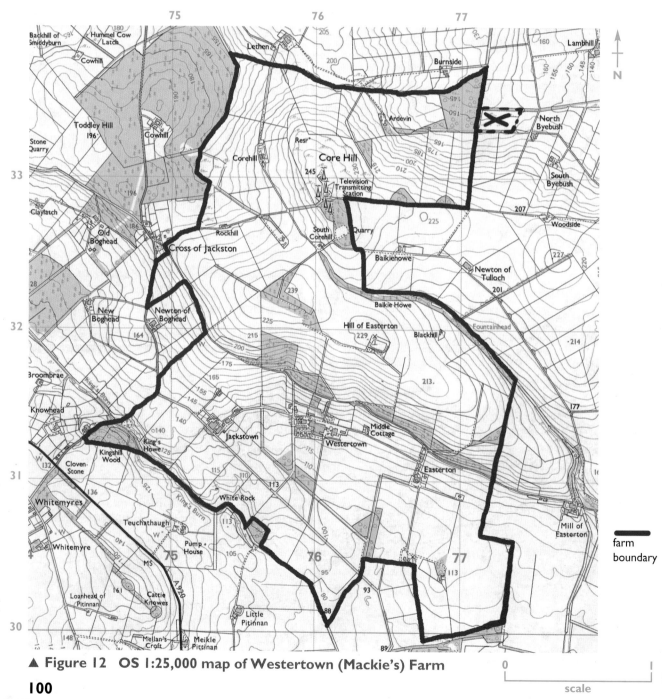

farm boundary

▲ **Figure 12 OS 1:25,000 map of Westertown (Mackie's) Farm**

# D   From cow to bowl: the making of Mackie's ice cream

The making of ice cream is a good example of a secondary or manufacturing industry. Ice cream does not occur naturally. It has to be made from milk and cream. The people who work in Mackie's ice cream parlour are workers in the secondary sector.

Have you ever wondered how ice cream is made? Figure 13 describes the whole process from beginning to end. The milk and cream from the cows are mixed together in the ice cream parlour (see Figure 13). The mixture is then heated to make sure that any harmful organisms are removed. It is then cooled and fruit may be added. The mixture is frozen in large freezers where it is whipped to introduce air. The air makes it taste smoother. Finally, the ice cream is poured into containers and deep-frozen. The whole process takes less than 24 hours and is largely computer-controlled.

Once frozen, the ice cream is taken by lorry to be distributed to shops. About 8 million litres of ice cream are produced every year at the farm. It is sold to Scotland, England and abroad to South Korea and Norway (see Figure 14).

Some people at Mackie's are involved with marketing and selling the ice cream (see Figure 13). They have to arrange all the advertising and they have to contact the shops that will sell the ice cream. They have to arrange for the ice cream to be collected from the farm and transported around the world. These jobs are tertiary sector jobs. You can now see how one single enterprise has examples of all three sectors of employment.

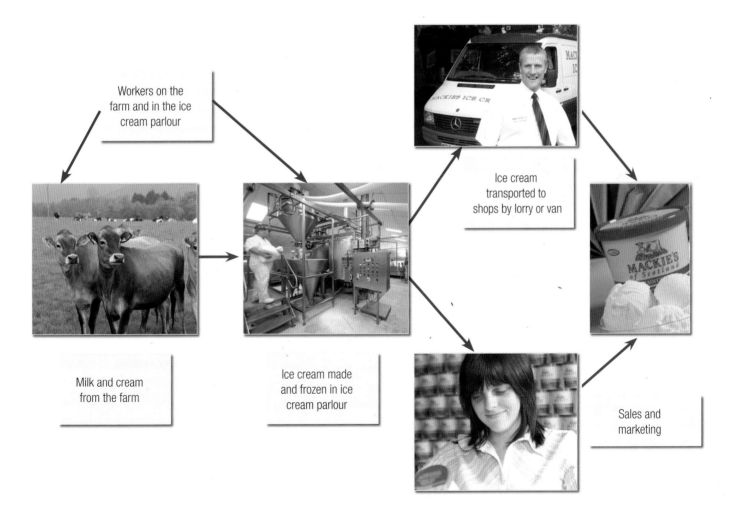

Workers on the farm and in the ice cream parlour

Ice cream transported to shops by lorry or van

Milk and cream from the farm

Ice cream made and frozen in ice cream parlour

Sales and marketing

▲ Figure 13   Mackie's ice cream flow diagram

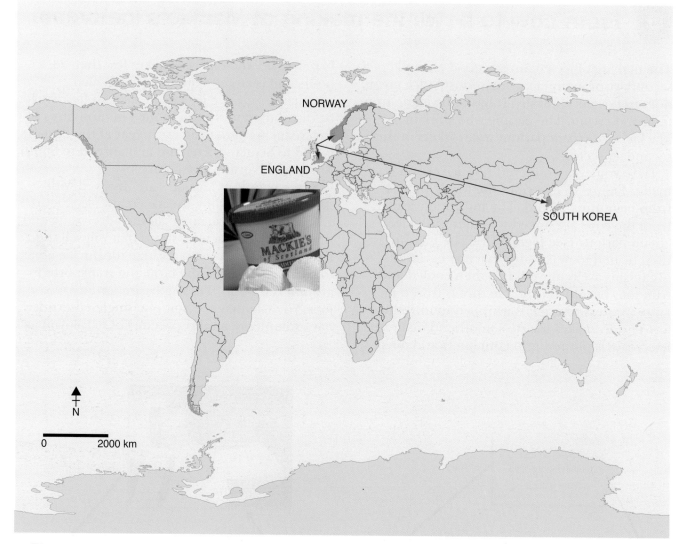

NORWAY

ENGLAND

SOUTH KOREA

N

0        2000 km

▲ Figure 14   Zoom map to show the distribution of Mackie's ice cream around the world

## Activities

6  Carefully re-read page 101 describing how ice cream is made.

a) Draw a series of boxes to produce a flow chart, showing how milk and cream is turned into ice cream in Mackie's ice cream parlour.

b) Suggest some types of fruit that might be added to the ice cream. Which one would be your favourite?

c) Do you think it is an advantage having the whole operation controlled by a computer? Explain your answer.

d) Assuming that 7 million litres of ice cream have been produced every year, how many million litres have been produced since the business started in 1993?

7  Study Figure 13.

a) What primary sector jobs are involved in making ice cream?

b) Suggest some tertiary sector jobs associated with making and selling ice cream.

c) Imagine that the company wishes to include strawberries in their ice cream. They are going to be grown in **polytunnels** on their farm. Why do you think it would be an advantage to grow their own strawberries rather than buying them from elsewhere?

d) In 1996, a New Product Development Kitchen was built. What do you think is its purpose?

e) Would jobs in the new kitchen be secondary or tertiary and why?

# E   Issue: How can Westertown Farm make extra money in the future?

Up until 1993, Westertown Farm concentrated on growing crops and producing milk from its herd of dairy cattle. However, in common with many farms in the UK in the 1990s, Westertown Farm was beginning to struggle to make much money from farming alone. So, it was decided to boost the farm's income by making luxury ice cream.

Elsewhere in the UK, farms have developed all sorts of schemes to provide extra income. This development is known as **farm diversification**.

Farmhouse bed-and-breakfast has become popular in recent years, especially with tourists from abroad. Farm outbuildings have been converted into holiday cottages, farm shops (see Figure 15) or small workshops for traditional arts and crafts. Fields have been developed into camping and caravan sites (Figure 16) or used for more adventurous activities, such as go-carting. Lakes have been stocked with fish or turned into nature reserves, with bird-watching hides and footpaths. Farms themselves have been opened to the public, with demonstrations of milking and animal petting areas.

▲ **Figure 15   Converted farm building**

## Activities

8  Study Figure 15, page 103.

   a)  Make a list of items for sale in the farm shop.

   b)  Why are farm shops becoming popular with shoppers nowadays?

   c)  What are the advantages to the farm of having a farm shop?

   d)  Can you suggest anything else that could be sold in the shop?

9  Work in pairs or small groups. You have been asked to suggest ways that Westertown Farm could diversify in the future. Your job is to write a report (electronic or handwritten) outlining your suggestions. You should make direct reference to the map (see Figure 12, page 100) and suggest where developments might take place on the farm. You must have sound reasons to back up your suggestions. Consider how people are going to travel to the farm and where they are going to park. You could include photographs of particular developments taken from the internet to illustrate your report. To gain the highest marks your report must be sensible and reasonable.

▲ **Figure 16   Farmland used for camping overlooking the sea**

# Energy

**In this chapter you will study:**

- sources of energy including renewable and non-renewable
- the formation of coal and its use in generating electricity
- the workings of a coal-fired power station
- conflicts associated with developing wind and tidal power
- energy conservation.

# A   What is energy?

Energy is needed to create power to make things work. We need energy to work and play. You have probably heard of 'high energy drinks' that are supposed to boost our energy and help us perform better in sport. Do you think they work?

The main source of energy is the sun. Plants capture this energy by carrying out the process of **photosynthesis** (see Figure 1). This energy is passed along the food chain (see Figure 9, page 17), for example, from a rabbit that eats the grass, to a fox that eats the rabbit.

When plants die they usually decompose. Look at what happens to grass cuttings on a compost heap – the plant nutrients are returned to the soil to help other plants grow. However, under certain conditions, plant remains may build up into great thicknesses without decomposing. Over millions of years, these plants and the energy trapped within are turned into **fossil fuels**, such as coal, oil and natural gas. Fossil fuels are called **non-renewable** resources as once they have been used they are gone forever. These resources are important sources of energy used throughout the world. They are burned to provide heat and power and they can be used to generate electricity.

Other sources of energy (such as the wind, the oceans and rivers) provide a constant supply of energy. They can be used over and over again without running out. For this reason they are called **renewable** energy sources.

Recently, people have become concerned about using non-renewable sources of energy. They are beginning to become more expensive and difficult to obtain. Also, when burned, they give off harmful gases which contribute to **global warming**. In the UK, the government is trying to increase the use of renewable sources of energy, especially wind power.

▲ Figure 1   Green plants photosynthesising

| | |
|---|---|
| 7.00am | Alarm goes off. Switch on light. Get dressed. |
| 7.30am | Put kettle onto the gas cooker to make a cup of tea and listen to the radio. |
| 7.35am | Make toast in the toaster. |
| 8.00am | Mum drives me to school – I listen to my iPod. |
| 9.00am | Watch a PowerPoint presentation in assembly. |
| 9.30am | Lessons. Lights on in most rooms. |
| 4.00pm | Used the computers after lunch. |
| 4.00pm | Climbing Club. Drive in minibus to outdoor climbing wall. Use up lots of energy scaling the wall! |
| 6.00pm | Dad collects me from school and drives me home. |
| 6.30pm | Mum cooks me tea. Sausage, eggs and beans. Yummee! |
| 7.30pm | Relax in front of a warm open fire to watch TV. Dad forces me to go outside into the cold to get some more coal for the fire! |

▲ Figure 2   Energy diary

## Activities

1 Consider how energy is used during a typical school day.
  a) Read the extract from an Energy Diary written by a Year 7 pupil (see Figure 2).
  b) For each entry in the diary identify the source of energy that is being used. Choose from coal, oil, gas or electricity.
  c) Write your own Energy Diary to see how important energy is in your daily life. Try to identify the source of energy being used.
  d) Imagine a world without electricity. Consider how your life would be different if electricity was not available. Write a few sentences describing how your everyday life would be different.
2 Study Figure 3, which shows a variety of energy sources.
  a) Sort the energy sources in Figure 3 into renewable and non-renewable. You can present your answer in the form of a table.
  b) Describe in your own words the difference between renewable and non-renewable energy.
  c) Do you think the government is right to encourage greater use of renewable energy in the UK? Explain your answer.

▲ Figure 3   Energy sources

# B The story of coal: a non-renewable form of energy

Coal is an example of a **non-renewable** energy source. It was formed millions of years ago from the accumulation of dead vegetation that once grew in vast tropical swamps. Over millions of years, great thicknesses of dead vegetation became buried, compressed and heated beneath many metres of sediment. Slowly the plant remains turned into solid black coal (see Figure 4).

Coal is a very valuable energy resource. It powered the Industrial Revolution in Europe in the nineteenth century (see Figure 5) and is today fuelling the massive economic growth in China and India (you will find out more about this in Year 9).

Up until the 1970s, coal was the main form of energy used in homes in the UK. Ask your grandparents about how they used coal in their homes. They will tell you that coal is dirty and heavy to carry. This explains why most coal in the UK is now burned in power stations to generate electricity.

▲ Figure 4   Coal mining in Derbyshire

Air pollution used to be a serious problem, with harmful gases such as sulphur dioxide being emitted. Nowadays, power stations have equipment installed to remove most of these polluting gases.

▲ Figure 5   The Industrial Revolution

The largest coal-fired power station producing electricity in the UK is at Drax, near Selby in North Yorkshire (see Figure 7). The huge power station employs 625 people. Its six generators produce 4000MW of electricity, which is about seven per cent of the UK's electricity needs.

Coal is brought into the power station by rail from UK coalfields and from sources abroad in Russia, South Africa and even Australia. It is used to heat water to produce steam. The steam drives the turbines to generate electricity. When cooled in the giant cooling towers, the steam turns into liquid water to be re-used in generating electricity. (You can see steam escaping from the cooling towers in Figure 7.)

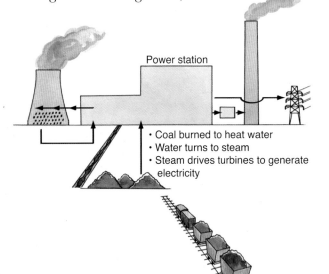

Power station
· Coal burned to heat water
· Water turns to steam
· Steam drives turbines to generate electricity

▲ Figure 6   Generating electricity from a coal-fired power station

▲ Figure 7   Drax power station

## Activities

3  Study Figure 6. It is a simplified diagram to show how electricity is generated at a coal-fired power station like Drax (see Figure 7).
   a) Make a large and careful copy of Figure 6.
   b) Write the following labels in their correct places. You will need to read them carefully to make sure that you place them correctly!
   ● Coal transported by train.
   ● Coal moved into the power station by conveyor belt.
   ● A precipitator takes out harmful gases before they enter the tall chimney.
   ● Tall chimney to release unwanted gases.
   ● Electricity pylons and transmission lines.
   ● Large circular cooling tower.
   ● Steam enters cooling tower and condenses.
   ● Water collects at base of cooling tower.
   ● Liquid water feeds into power station.
   ● Steam escapes from the cooling tower.

4  Study your completed diagram of Figure 6 and the photograph of the power station (Figure 7).
   a) Why does the power station need to be built on a large area of flat land?
   b) Suggest why coal is transported to the power station by rail.
   c) Look at Figure 7. Next to which river has the power station been built?
   d) Why is it important for the power station to have a nearby supply of water?
   e) Why do you think the power station has a tall chimney to release the unwanted gases?

# C  Wind power: a renewable form of energy

The UK is well known as a very windy place. In the past, the wind was used to power windmills that ground wheat into flour for making bread (see Figure 8). More recently, a modern version of the windmill called a **wind turbine** has become a common sight in the countryside (Figure 9).

Figure 9 shows the three wind turbines on Westertown Farm (see Chapter 8). There are really tall measuring some 45 metres in height. This is about the same height as a ten-storey building! Unlike the huge sweeping sails of the windmill in Figure 8, the wind turbines have three quite slender 25-metre blades, which can be turned to face into the wind. The wind turns the turbines' blades to produce electricity.

The government is keen to promote the use of wind power to reduce our reliance on fossil fuels such as coal, oil and gas. Clusters of wind turbines called **wind farms** have sprung up across the UK (Figure 10). There are plans to build a huge wind farm in the sea off the coast of Kent.

Whilst wind turbines are non-polluting, some people consider them to be ugly. Proposals for new wind farms are often strongly opposed by local people. Additionally, wind turbines cannot work in very light breezes or strong winds. They can be expensive to build and a vast number are required to produce meaningful amounts of electricity. They are however particularly effective at the very local scale such as on Westertown Farm.

▲ **Figure 8   Traditional windmill**

▲ **Figure 9   Wind turbines, Westertown Farm**

## Activities

5  Study Figures 8, 9 and 10.

  a) Some old windmills in the UK are owned and preserved by organisations like the National Trust. Do you think this is a good idea? Explain your answer.

  b) Would you be interested to visit an old windmill? Why?

  c) Do you prefer the look of windmills or wind turbines? Give reasons for your answer.

  d) Draw a sketch of one of the wind turbines in Figure 10 (page 110). Add labels to show its main features.

  e) How do you think the land around the turbines is being used in Figure 9?

6  For this activity you will need to turn to the OS map of Westertown Farm (Figure 12, page 100).

  a) One of the wind turbines in Figure 9 is marked on the map, using a single symbol in grid square 7631. What is the symbol?

  b) Why do you think the wind turbines are located here? (Hint: Remember that the prevailing wind blows from the southwest.)

  c) Imagine there are plans to build two new turbines on Westertown Farm. Assume that the other two are located together. Can you suggest a good location elsewhere on the farm? Give reasons for your answer.

## Activities

7  Study Figure 10. It includes a list of arguments for and against wind farms. The arguments have been mixed up!

   a) Read through the statements and sort them correctly into two lists: for and against.

   b) Imagine that a wind farm was due to be constructed in an area of countryside near to where you live. How would you feel about such a proposal? Explain your answer.

   c) Increasingly, wind farms are being built offshore in the sea. Why do you think this is becoming a popular option?

### ICT ACTIVITY

Carry out a study of wind speeds in your school grounds. To find out whether your school may be a suitable site for a wind turbine, work through page 5 of the renewable energy audit at:

**https://www.redcar-cleveland. gov.uk/pdf/Renewable%20Energy %20Audit%20-%20schools.pdf**

i   They are an eyesore spoiling the natural landscape

ii  Turbines can sometimes be heard to make a humming noise

iii Turbines take up little space allowing other land uses to occur on the same land, such as farming

iv  Wind turbines are sleek and interesting to look at

v   Turbines are expensive to install

vi  Turbines are non-polluting to the atmosphere

vii Turbines cannot work during low or very high winds

viii The UK has a windy climate

▲ **Figure 10   Wind farm, near Inverness Scotland**

### ICT ACTIVITY

Use the internet to find out how electricity can be generated by one type of renewable energy of your choice, such as solar, waves, biomass, hydro-power or geothermal. (Don't study wind or tidal power as these are both covered in this chapter.)

Your research enquiry should try to answer the following questions:

• How is electricity generated?

• Why is it a renewable source of energy?

• What are the advantages and disadvantages of this source of energy?

• Where in the UK is it or could it be used?

Before making your choice of which energy source to investigate, spend some time searching for information. Use the weblinks below to help you get started.

There is an excellent site below (developed by a science teacher) which has lots of information on all the alternative energy sources, with good diagrams and links to other sites:

**http://www.darvill.clara.net/altenerg/index.htm**

Other sites include:

National Energy Foundation

**http://www.nef.org.uk/greenenergy/index.htm**

BBC Weather Centre has information at

**http://www.bbc.co.uk/climate/adaptation**

Remember! You will not be credited for simply cutting and pasting information.

# D Conserving energy

We live in a world of ever-increasing energy demands. With our need for heating, lighting and air conditioning, the use of electricity has increased dramatically in recent years. Think of all the items that you use at home and at school that need electricity. Now consider the use of energy for transport, such as cars and aeroplanes. As the world's population grows and people become richer, the demand for energy will increase still further.

One way to cope with the increasing demand for energy is to use it more efficiently and avoid wasting it. This is called **energy conservation**.

## Activities

8 Study Figure 11. Suggest ways of conserving energy in the home.
  a) Make a simple copy of the house shown in Figure 11.
  b) Complete the diagram by adding the following energy conservation labels in their correct places:
   ● Insulate the loft space with up to 25 cm of insulation
   ● Double-glaze windows to reduce heat loss
   ● Replace old electrical items (such as fridges) with more energy efficient appliances
   ● Use low energy light bulbs
   ● Do not leave TVs and computers on 'standby'.
  c) Write a short report to accompany your diagram to summarise what can be done to conserve energy in the house. Use the internet to discover additional ways of reducing energy use in the home. Add additional labels if you wish. A Google search 'energy conservation in the home' will reveal several sites including Colorado State University at: http://www.ext.colostate.edu/pubs/consumer/10610.html.

9 Conduct an energy audit in your home.
  a) Use the knowledge that you have gained from Activity 8 to make a list of ways in which energy is currently being conserved at home.
  b) Now make a list of other ways in which energy could be conserved in the future.
  c) What action do you think should be taken next to increase energy conservation in your home? Explain your answer.

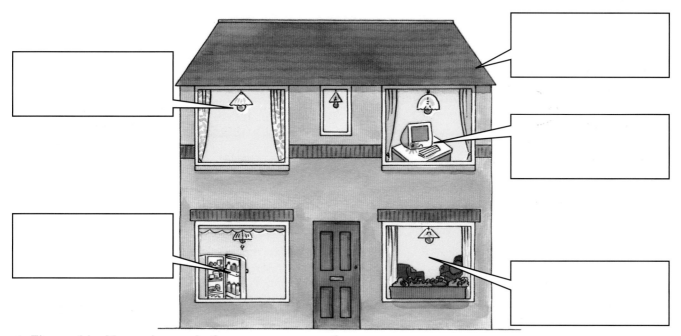

▲ **Figure 11  House in need of energy conservation**

# E   Issue: Should the Severn Barrage be built?

The River Severn has the second highest tidal range in the world. The tidal range is the difference in height between high tide and low tide. The River Severn has a tidal range of over 12.5 m!

There have been several proposals to make use of the River Severn's extreme tidal range to generate electricity. The most recent proposal involves constructing a low 10-mile-long dam or barrage across the River Severn near Weston-super-Mare in Somerset (see Figure 12).

The barrage would hold back the water as the tide fell. This would form a raised lake on the upstream side of the barrage. Gates in the dam would then be opened to allow the water to rush through, turning turbines to generate electricity (Figure 13).

The proposal is very controversial. The table to the right outlines some of the advantages and disadvantages of the scheme.

## Activity

10  Work individually or in pairs.
   a) Read through this section first. Now decide whether or not you think the Severn Barrage should be built.
   b) Write a letter to a local newspaper outlining your point of view. If you support the proposal, you could take the position of the Severn Tidal Power Group (who have made the most recent proposal). If you are against the plan, you could take the position of the RSPB.

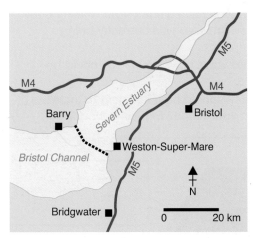

▲ **Figure 12   Location of proposed Severn Barrage**

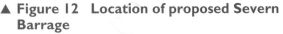
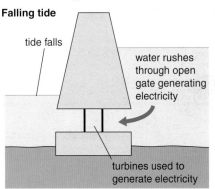

▲ **Figure 13   How tides are used to generate electricity**

| Advantages and disadvantages of the Severn Barrage | |
|---|---|
| **Advantages** | **Disadvantages** |
| Tidal power is renewable and will last forever. | The barrage could have a harmful impact on the natural ecosystems adjacent to the river. |
| The barrage itself will have a life of 120 years. | An estimated 65,000 water-birds currently visit the Severn Estuary. The RSPB is concerned that important inter-tidal feeding grounds for birds will be affected. |
| The government is committed to producing more electricity from renewable sources. This will reduce the UK's dependence on fossil fuels and reduce emissions of greenhouse gases. | The famous 'Severn Bore' (a small tidal wave that sweeps up the River Severn several times a year) may stop. |
| Tidal power is non-polluting. It will not contribute to global warming. | The barrage would have a significant negative impact on the natural landscape of the area. |
| The barrage could provide 6 per cent of electricity in England and Wales. | The cost of building the barrage (an estimated £14 billion) would be huge and could outweigh the benefits. Other forms of renewable energy could be more cost-effective. |
| The barrage could be dual-purpose and be used to help protect low-lying coastal areas upstream from rising sea levels (associated with global warming). | The transport of construction materials to the site (such as rock aggregate) could require changes to be made to nearby docks in Bristol and Cardiff. |
| Construction of the barrage will create jobs. | Construction of the barrage, and economic developments after the barrage has been built, will create greenhouse gases. |

# Leisure and Recreation

**In this chapter you will study:**

- quality of life – the work/life balance
- sport for all
- seaside resorts: Blackpool
- managing Stonehenge.

# A Quality of life: the work/life balance

Consider for a moment what affects your quality of life. You would probably include food, home life, friends, school and even the amount of homework you have been set. In many parts of the world, children of your age have a very low quality of life (see Figure 1). They may not have enough food; they may live on the street and have no family. They may live in constant fear of being hurt or abused. In comparison, you are very lucky.

You are especially lucky in being able to make choices. Whilst you may spend a lot of time at school, you do have a huge amount of spare time (particularly at weekends and during holidays). You can choose what to do in your spare time. It is during our spare time that we take part in leisure or recreational activities (see Figure 2).

Many people consider that it is important to have a balance between work and play. This is often called the **work/life balance**. Some people spend too much of their time at work, and this can have a bad effect on their health and on their family and friends. Just as with the food we eat, keeping a balance between work and leisure is important if we are to have a high quality of life.

## Activities

1 Make a list of the things that affect your quality of life. Select the five most important things. List them in order of importance (this is called **ranking**). Compare your list with others in your class.

2 Study the photograph in Figure 1. What do you think are the five most important things affecting the quality of life of these children?

3 Complete a leisure diary for a week.

   a) Draw up a daily record sheet to record what you do in your spare time. Most of this will be in the evenings and at weekends. Try to give approximate times.

   b) Add up the hours spent on your various leisure activities. Represent this information in the form of a suitable graph.

   c) Do the results surprise you?

   d) How do you think your leisure diary would be different during other times of the year (e.g. different seasons and during school holidays)?

▲ **Figure 1   Street children in Brazil**

▲ **Figure 2 Leisure activities**

## LOCAL FIELDWORK

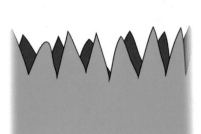

**Find out about opportunities for leisure and recreation in your local area. To do this you will need to obtain a detailed map (a 1:25,000 OS map will be fine).**

● Look closely at the map and try to identify opportunities for leisure and recreation (such as green spaces, footpaths, recreation grounds and sports centres).

● On a black and white copy of the map (or using tracing paper), use a colour to shade the places and areas you have identified. Are some areas better served by opportunities for leisure and recreation than others? Why do you think this is so?

● As a class, visit a nearby green area (such as a park) to identify the opportunities for leisure and recreation. Record the activities that are available in the park. Plot them onto a base map. What facilities are available for people to use (such as toilets, changing rooms and benches)? How could the park be improved?

● Work in pairs or small groups. Re-design a nearby park to improve the way it serves the local community. Consider what activities you think should be on offer. What facilities will be needed? Now design your park on a large sheet of plain paper.

# B  Sport for all

Many of us enjoy taking part in sport during our spare time. This might involve playing sport competitively (such as being in a football team), or taking part in sport for fun (such as horse riding, hiking, or cycling). Some people enjoy travelling to watch sporting events (such as Wimbledon tennis). Apart from its health benefits, sport has social benefits too, as we meet new people and spend time with our friends.

With so many people wishing to take part in sport, it is important to have enough local facilities available. These include informal parks for walking, cycling and playing tennis (see Figure 3), skateboard and BMX parks (see Figure 4), indoor sports centres and swimming pools.

As people in the UK have increasing amounts of spare time and more money to spend, planning for sport has become a major geographical issue. Turn to page 88 to read about the plans for the 2012 Olympic games in London.

▲ Figure 4  BMX park

▲ Figure 3  Park with opportunities for sport and leisure activities

## Sheffield, National City of Sport

In 1995 Sheffield was named the first National City of Sport. The city is home to a great range of high quality sporting venues. It also has centres for sports research, sports medicine and sports engineering.

Several major sporting venues are located in the Lower Don Valley (see the map in Figure 5). This area once housed the heavy steelmaking industries that brought Sheffield its wealth and led to the growth of the city.

Its tradition as a steelmaking city is reflected by the name of its ice hockey team, 'The Steelers'. During the late twentieth century many of these heavy industries closed down due to competition from abroad and the land became derelict. Extensive redevelopment of the Lower Don valley in recent years has included the building of large sporting arenas such as the Don Valley Stadium (see Figure 5).

In 2004 Sheffield City Council launched a Masterplan for the Lower Don Valley. Over the next 20 years new housing, industries and roads will be constructed providing jobs for 17,000 people. Green areas and pathways will link these mixed-use areas.

## Activity

4 Create a class wall display to show the sports that each pupil has physically taken part in or been to see recently (and not just watched on TV). To do this, each person needs to take and then print a photograph which shows either them taking part in a sporting activity, or watching a sport. These photographs can then be displayed on the classroom wall, possibly located onto a map of the area. Alternatively, a similar class record could be posted on the school's intranet.

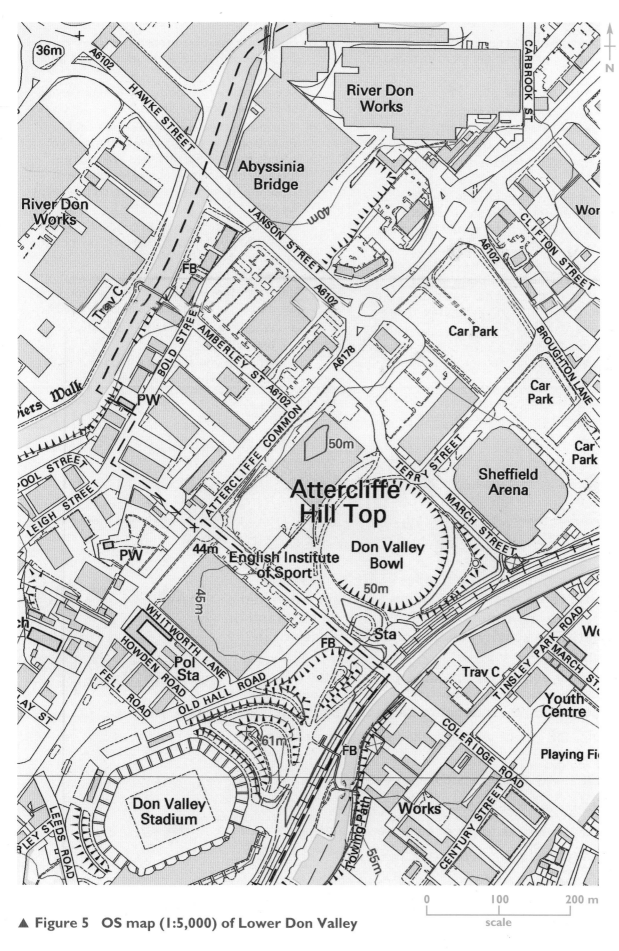

▲ Figure 5   OS map (1:5,000) of Lower Don Valley

5 The UK government and medical organisations are encouraging people to get more involved in sport.

   a) Why do you think this is?

   b) Suggest ways that more people could be encouraged to take part in sport.

   c) What should local planning authorities do to make it possible for more people to take part in sport?

   d) Design a T-shirt to encourage people to take part in sport. The T-shirt should have a powerful message, but it should look good too!

6 Study Figure 5. It shows some of the developments in the Lower Don Valley. The waterway in the top left of the map extract is the River Don. The waterway in the bottom right is the Sheffield and Tinsley Canal.

   a) Locate the River Don Works. Suggest reasons why this site was chosen for the factories.

   b) Suggest a possible problem with the site of these industrial buildings. (Hint – think about the river!)

   c) Make a list of the sports and leisure facilities shown on the map extract.

   d) You are on the Abyssinia Bridge over the River Don. You have arranged to meet your friends outside the Sheffield Arena at the junction of Terry Street and March Street. Describe the route that you would take. How far is it?

   e) Use map evidence only to suggest why the Lower Don Valley is a good location for large sporting arenas.

   f) Locate the River Don Works to the west of the River Don. Imagine that these Works were to close and the buildings demolished.

     ● What might be suitable new uses for this land?

     ● What do you suggest should be located here and why?

## LOCAL FIELDWORK

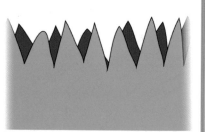

**Find out about the opportunities for sport in your local town or city. To do this you will need to obtain a detailed map of the area and conduct some research on foot (and on the internet). This activity can be done individually or in small groups.**

The aim of your enquiry is to produce an annotated map locating and describing the activities available locally. You can include photos from the internet or take some photos yourself.

Having completed your map, discuss the following questions in your class:

● Does your town/city have a good range of sporting venues?

● Are there opportunities for informal sports at a local level?

● Are some parts of your town/city better served than others?

● Are some sports better served than others?

● Is there a need for a particular sporting venue? If so, where could it be located?

## C   Seaside resort: Blackpool

Blackpool is a large town on the northwest coast of England (see Figure 6). It is one of Europe's top seaside resorts. Every year, over 16.5 million people come to the town to enjoy the famous Pleasure Beach, the 'Golden Mile' promenade (see Figure 7) and to visit the piers, funfairs and the famous Blackpool Tower. In the autumn, the seafront is lit spectacularly at night by the Blackpool Illuminations.

▲ **Figure 7   Blackpool promenade (modern)**

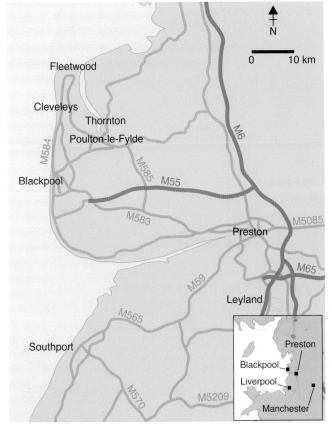

▲ **Figure 6   Location of Blackpool**

**Figure 8   Blackpool promenade (early 1900s)**

### Activities

7  Study Figure 8.

   a) What tourist attractions can you see in the photograph?

   b) Do you think the people in the photograph are relatively rich or poor? Explain your answer.

   c) Describe the surface of the main promenade.

   d) Apart from by foot, what is the other form of transport shown in the photograph?

   e) Look closely at the buildings on the righthand side of the photograph. How does the ground floor use of the buildings differ from the other storeys?

   f) If you were able to time travel, would you like to visit Blackpool during this time? Explain your answer.

8  Spot the difference! Study Figures 7 and 8 and work with a friend to list as many differences as you can between the two photographs.

The name 'Blackpool' dates back to the Middle Ages when the area was no more than a boggy swamp. A stream in the area created a pool, tainted black by the peaty ground, hence the name 'black pool'. In its early days, it was fishing that led to the growth of the settlement. However, the area soon became popular with local visitors attracted by the golden beaches.

● In 1846 the railway arrived. This led to mass tourism from the nearby Lancashire and Yorkshire mill towns. The piers and the Tower were built.

● By the end of the nineteenth century the population was 40,000 and tourism was big business. The population reached 150,000 by the 1960s.

● From the 1970s, population has declined as people have had more freedom to travel further afield.

● In 2002 Blackpool launched a masterplan 'Vision for the Future' to regenerate the resort. It has received a huge amount of investment and is now a conference centre as well as a tourist resort.

| Year | Current total population |
|------|--------------------------|
| 1801 | 1,881 |
| 1821 | 2,704 |
| 1841 | 3,837 |
| 1861 | 8,044 |
| 1881 | 15,163 |
| 1901 | 39,285 |
| 1921 | 80,971 |
| 1941 | 123,801 |
| 1961 | 149,474 |
| 1981 | 145,784 |
| 2001 | 142,284 |

http://www.visionofbritain.org.uk

**Figure 9   Population growth in Blackpool (1801 to 2001)**

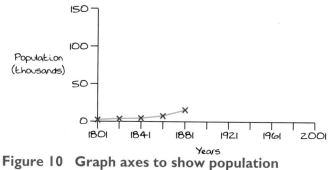

**Figure 10   Graph axes to show population growth in Blackpool (1801 to 2001)**

## Activities

**9  Study Figure 9.**

a) Use the information in Figure 9 to plot a line graph to show the growth of Blackpool's population. Figure 10 shows the graph axes and the first few points. Notice that the time scale on the bottom axis is constant. Make the graph as big as possible on your page.

b) Add the following labels in their correct places to help to explain the early growth in the population.
  ● 1846 railway arrives in Blackpool
  ● 1868 Blackpool Central Pier built
  ● 1894 Blackpool Tower built

c) Write a few sentences describing the trend of the graph.

d) What is being done to try to reverse the recent decline in Blackpool's population?

**10  Study Figure 11.**

a) What form of transport operates along the promenade?

b) What is the tourist attraction at the Central Pier?

c) On what road are most of the main banks found?

d) Imagine that you and your family were in Blackpool during a wet morning. Select two places that you would choose to visit. Explain your choices.

e) How is traffic managed in the centre of Blackpool?

f) You have just visited the Tower and wish to walk to the Post Office to buy some stamps for postcards. Describe the shortest route to the Post Office.

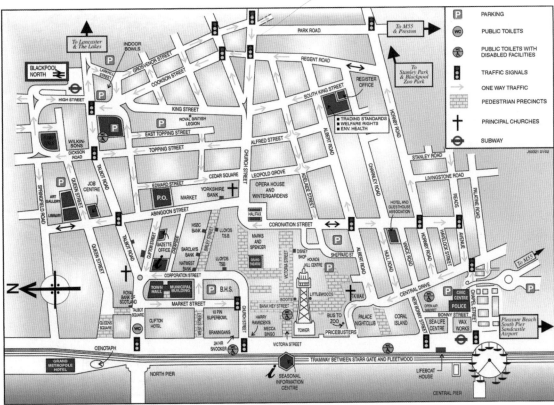

Source: *Blackpool Borough Council*

**Figure 11   Town map of Blackpool**

## ICT ACTIVITY

1  The aim of this activity is to produce a tourist brochure to advertise Blackpool to families living in your local area. Imagine that the finished brochure will be made available in your local town libraries and information centres. It is important that you focus on the kinds of things that families would be interested in doing.

You first need to find out what Blackpool has to offer tourists. To do this you should access the Visit Blackpool website at: http://www.visitblackpool.com.

Other good websites include About Britain at: http://www.aboutbritain.com/towns/blackpool.asp and Tourist Net at: http://www.touristnetuk.com/NW/blackpool.

Take time to design your brochure carefully, so that it is both attractive and informative.

2  Imagine that you are going to visit Blackpool for a weekend in the summer holidays. Your parents (who are no good with computers!) have asked you to help find the following information:

- **Train times:** for travel from your local station to Blackpool. Use the National Rail Enquiries website at http://www.nationalrail.co.uk to find appropriate trains and fares for your family.

- **Accommodation:** use the various Blackpool tourist websites to find accommodation in Blackpool for Friday and Saturday night. You are looking for a relatively cheap family room in a hotel with bed and breakfast. A further source of accommodation is an agency such as Superbreak at: http://www.superbreak.com/index.htm.

- **Attractions:** for you to visit while you are there. Put together an itinerary of places to visit and things to do for the Saturday and the Sunday morning, before your return rail journey. Remember, you will need time to move from one attraction to the other, so do not plan to do too much. Obtain a map to help you find your way around (see Figure 11).

## D   Issue: How should Stonehenge be managed sustainably?

Stonehenge is one of several **World Heritage Sites** in the UK (see Figure 12). World Heritage Sites are internationally-important, cultural or natural sites that are protected to ensure that they remain intact for future generations. Look at Figure 12. Notice that these sites include ancient castles, historic buildings and natural landscapes.

Stonehenge is one of the most famous prehistoric sites in the UK. Its familiar stone circle (see Figure 13) dates back to 3100BC. Nobody knows for certain why it was built. Some people think it was an important religious meeting place, others believe it was connected to astronomy and the science of the stars.

Today, Stonehenge is a popular tourist attraction, with over 800,000 people visiting it each year. For some people Stonehenge is a spiritual site as well as one of immense historical importance. For example, many people gather at Stonehenge for the Summer Solstice.

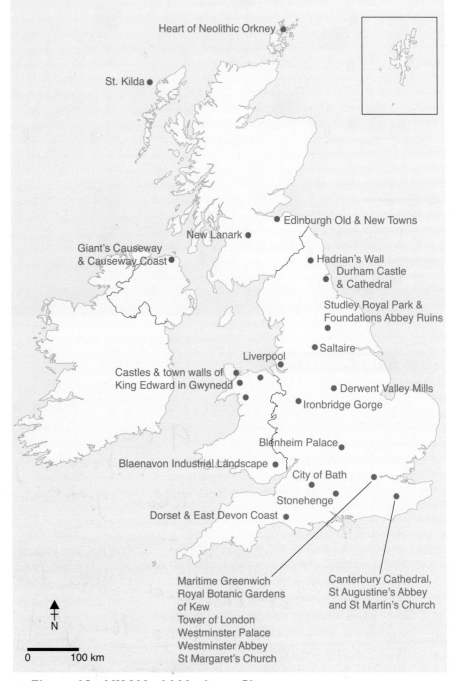

▲ **Figure 12   UK World Heritage Sites**

With so many people wishing to visit Stonehenge, there are a number of management issues.

- There is too much visitor pressure on the area immediately adjacent to the stone circle.

- There are not enough car parking spaces or public facilities, such as toilets and food outlets. Water supply is a real issue.

- The area is heavily congested with people and cars, causing local pollution.

- The many smaller archaeological sites in the area are not very accessible and are often overlooked by visitors.

- Some of the land is ploughed by farmers, which may cause damage.

In the light of these issues, a management plan has been drawn up to ensure a sustainable future for the site. The main features of the plan include:

- The world heritage site (Figure 14 on page 124) will become a core area, with controlled access to the main stone circle and the other smaller archaeological sites.

- The site will be used for permanent pasture only, with no ploughing allowed.

- A new visitor centre will be built outside the core area. It will have a large car park and facilities for refreshments and toilets. There will be an interpretation centre to help people understand more about the site.

- Footpaths and drop-off points will be created, to give people access to the core area. There will be facilities for visitors with disabilities.

- There will be numerous information boards to help people interpret the site.

- The main A303 road may be re-routed in a tunnel beneath the site.

▲ **Figure 13   Stonehenge stone circle**

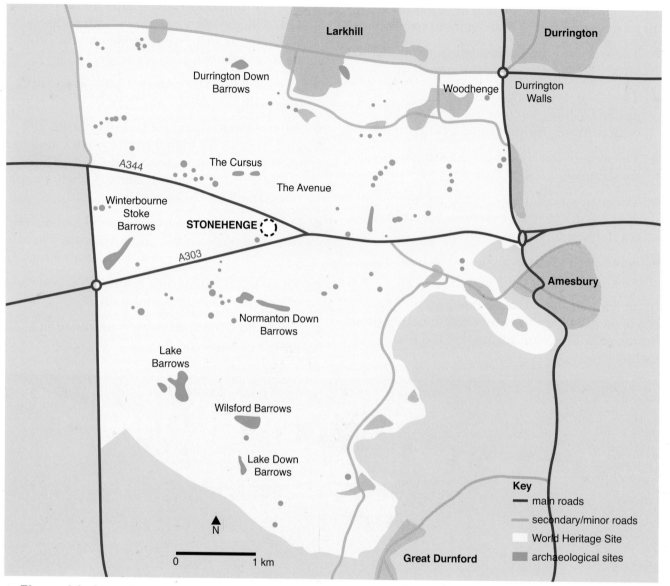

▲ **Figure 14   Location of Stonehenge**

## Activities

11  Work in pairs or small groups. Draw a new map of the site based on Figure 14, to show what it could look like in the future if the management plan goes ahead. To do this you will need to use a large base map of Figure 14 (or a sheet of tracing paper to act as an overlay). Discuss and then draw on the following features:

a) The re-routed main roads – possibly involving a tunnel.

b) The location of the new visitor centre – think carefully about its location (it will need to have plenty of land available and good road access); make use of internet maps (Google or Multimap) to help with your decision.

c) A bus route – from the visitor centre to the main archaeological sites; to provide access for the elderly, the young and those with physical disabilities (you may wish to create a ring route).

d) The footpaths – to give access to the main sites.

e) The seats and information boards – choose their location carefully.

Your completed map can then be presented to the rest of the class for discussion.

# Environment

**In this chapter you will study:**

- the issue of waste
- what is rubbish?
- the three 'Rs': reduce, reuse and recycle
- recycling in the UK
- how to recycle more aluminium.

## A   What a waste

Look at the photograph in Figure 1. It shows a pile of rubbish that has been dumped in the countryside. How many different items of rubbish can you see? The dumping of **waste** is called **fly tipping**. Apart from being illegal, fly tipping is extremely harmful to the environment. Toxic chemicals or broken glass bottles may harm animals and birds. The soil and underground water sources may become polluted. Dumps like these are also very unattractive and spoil the countryside (Figure 2).

Did you know that each week an average family gets through four glass bottles or jars, thirteen cans, three plastic bottles and five kilograms of paper. This means that in England and Wales, 8000 tonnes of rubbish are thrown away every day of the year, which is the same weight as 1600 African elephants!

Did you know that 8 to 9 million disposable nappies are thrown away each year in the UK, and that each one takes 500 years to decompose if buried in the ground?

▲ **Figure 1   Fly tipping**

### Activity

1 Study the photograph in Figure 1.
  a) Make a list of the different types of rubbish that have been dumped on the ground.
  b) Why do you think people dump their rubbish?
  c) Look at the cartoon in Figure 2. What point do you think is being made by the artist?

There is increasing concern about the amount of waste that we produce and about how to best dispose of it. In this chapter, we shall explore some of the issues involved with sustainable waste management.

"It's the kind of beautiful Sunday afternoon that makes me want to visit our favourite beauty spot and dump lots of rubbish"

Source: *www.CartoonStock.com*

▲ **Figure 2   Cartoon on fly tipping**

### ICT ACTIVITY

Imagine that you have been asked to write a front-page article for a local newspaper about the problem of fly tipping. Conduct an internet search to find a photograph of fly tipping. Think of a good title and write a few sentences to describe the harm that fly tipping may cause to the environment.

## LOCAL FIELDWORK

### Find out about the problem of litter in your school grounds.

For this activity you will need a plan of your school grounds, with a grid superimposed over it. The size of each grid square will depend upon your school but somewhere between 2 to 5 square metres should work. Work in pairs (you will probably be allocated a part of the school).

- Visit the grid squares and record how much litter you find. Use the key in Figure 3 (or make up your own key) and write the appropriate number in each grid square on a copy of the school plan. (An alternative is to record the litter that *can be seen* from each grid square or sample point. This would give you a measure of *visual pollution*. You could use the same categories suggested in Figure 3.)

- Take digital photographs of the worst areas of littering, which can then be labelled.

- Record the position of any litter bins.

- On a blank version of the school plan, use the colours suggested in the key to colour the grid squares according to the number recorded in the field.

- Write a few sentences describing the distribution of litter in your school grounds. Try to suggest reasons for its distribution. Suggest some action that could be taken by your school to reduce the problem.

| Reference number | Description | Colour |
|---|---|---|
| 0 | no litter | leave blank (white) |
| 1 | **Minor litter problem:** 1 or 2 small pieces of litter (e.g. sweet wrappers) | yellow |
| 2 | **Moderate litter problem:** 3 to 10 pieces of litter (possibly including drinks cans or cartons, waste paper, card) | orange |
| 3 | **Major litter problem:** more than 10 pieces of litter (possibly including lots of sweet wrappers, drinks cans, waste paper, card, plastic bags) | red |

▲ **Figure 3   Litter categories**

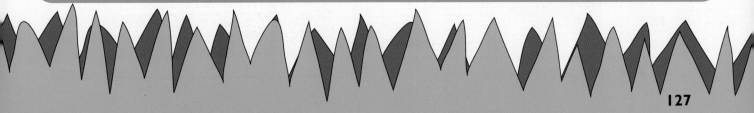

## B   What is rubbish?

Rubbish is everything that you throw away or no longer have a use for (for example, an empty packet of crisps, a used ink cartridge, a damaged CD or a punctured football). Rubbish can be solid, liquid or gas.

There are a number of different types of rubbish. Rubbish produced from our homes is called **domestic waste**. It is made up mostly of paper, card, plastics and glass. Figure 4 shows the contents of a typical dustbin. **Industrial** or commercial waste (again, mostly paper and card) comes from factories, offices and schools. Dangerous or **hazardous waste**, such as chemicals used to make paint, has to be disposed of very carefully.

Some rubbish, such as kitchen waste, paper and grass cuttings, is **biodegradable** and will naturally rot down. Other rubbish, such as cans, glass and plastics are **non-biodegradable** and will not break down naturally.

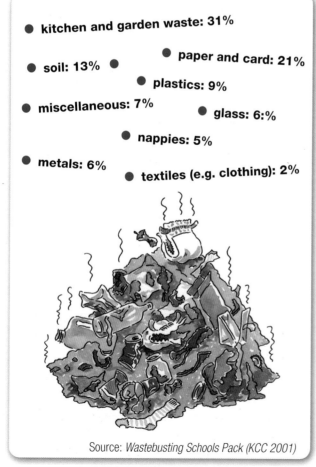

- **kitchen and garden waste: 31%**
- **soil: 13%**
- **paper and card: 21%**
- **plastics: 9%**
- **miscellaneous: 7%**
- **glass: 6:%**
- **nappies: 5%**
- **metals: 6%**
- **textiles (e.g. clothing): 2%**

Source: *Wastebusting Schools Pack (KCC 2001)*

▲ **Figure 4  Contents of dustbin**

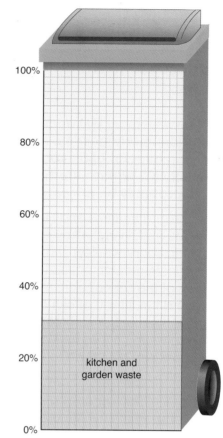

▲ **Figure 5   Dustbin graph**

### Activity

2   Study Figure 4.

a)   Make a copy of the graph box in Figure 5 on a sheet of graph paper. Use the data in Figure 4 to complete a divided bar graph to show the typical contents of a domestic dustbin.

b)   What do you think makes up kitchen waste?

c)   Suggest some different forms of plastic that might end up in the bin.

d)   The word 'miscellaneous' means other items not listed. Can you suggest some miscellaneous items that might be thrown away?

e)   Nowadays, several types of rubbish that used to end up in the bin are now separated for recycling. What types of rubbish are recycled where you live?

f)   Take a look (not too close!) at the contents of your main bin at home. What are the main items of rubbish?

## **C** Where does our rubbish go?

The bulk of our rubbish ends up in huge holes in the ground called **landfill sites** (see Figure 6). Waste is transported to these sites (often, abandoned quarries) by refuse lorries. The waste is compacted and over several years the hole is filled in. It is then covered over with a layer of soil, grassed and often used as land for grazing. Special care has to be taken to remove harmful chemicals and gases produced by the rotting rubbish (see Figure 7).

▲ **Figure 6   Landfill site**

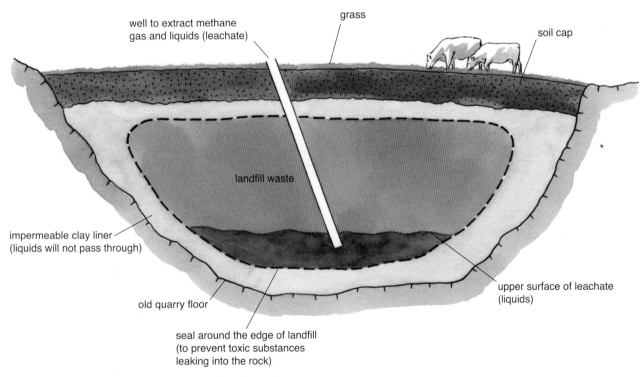

well to extract methane gas and liquids (leachate)

grass

soil cap

landfill waste

impermeable clay liner (liquids will not pass through)

old quarry floor

seal around the edge of landfill (to prevent toxic substances leaking into the rock)

upper surface of leachate (liquids)

▲ **Figure 7   Landfill site restored for farming**

### Activity

3  Study Figures 6 and 7.

a) Why are old quarries often chosen as landfill sites?

b) What is the purpose of the impermeable clay liner?

c) What is 'leachate'?

d) What is the name of the gas that can build up to become dangerously explosive in landfill sites?

e) After it is full, a landfill site is reclaimed and used for another purpose. How is the landfill site in Figure 7 being used?

f) The lack of suitable landfill sites is a big issue in waste management in the UK. Why do you think landfill sites are running out?

g) What do you think should be done about this problem and why?

h) What do you find the most striking feature of the landfill site in Figure 6?

## D Reduce, reuse and recycle

The world has limited resources and it is important that we make the best use of them. If we continue to use resources wastefully, future generations will suffer shortages. We need to adopt a more sustainable approach. This means using less and, wherever possible, reusing or recycling. The phrase that is often used to describe this approach is **reduce, reuse and recycle** (the '3 Rs'). A sustainable approach to waste management means that future generations (your children and grandchildren) will not have to suffer because of our thoughtless actions. Resources will still be available and the environment will not have been damaged.

▲ **Figure 8   Shopping items**

There are several ways of reducing waste. For example, we should use less packaging on goods available in shops. Consider how the items that your family buys from supermarkets often have multi-layered packaging (see Figure 8). Once an item has been used for its original purpose it can often be reused rather than being thrown away. By reusing items the amount of waste thrown away is reduced. Figure 9 describes some popular ways of reusing items. Once items no longer have a use to us they are then thrown away. A good many items, such as paper, card, glass, drinks cans and kitchen waste, do not have to be dumped in landfills. They can instead be separated and recycled.

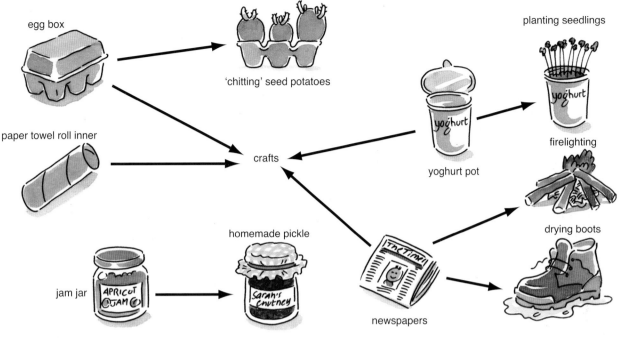

egg box

'chitting' seed potatoes

planting seedlings

paper towel roll inner

crafts

yoghurt pot

firelighting

drying boots

jam jar   APRICOT JAM

homemade pickle   Sarah's Chutney

newspapers

▲ **Figure 9  Reusing household items**

## Activities

4  Study the amount of packaging that is brought into your home.

   a)  Make a copy of the table below to record the packaging on up to 20 items brought into your home during the course of a week.

   b)  Analyse the packaging around each item and record the details in your table. There is no need to analyse more than 20 items, but try to include some variety.

   c)  Combine your results with others in your class to find out:
   - the average amount of packaging (layers)
   - the breakdown of the packaging materials used (which materials are used the most)
   - which items are overpackaged.

   You could represent the information in the form of graphs (such as bar charts).

   d)  Write a short report (based on your findings) under the following title: 'Is there too much packaging on items bought from shops?'

(This activity is based on a Packaging Audit activity developed by Recycle-More. See the website at **http://www.recycle-more.co.uk/** for further interesting activities and useful materials.)

5  Work in pairs to produce a logo to be displayed in school encouraging people to 'reduce, reuse and recycle'.

   a)  Spend some time discussing the content and design of your logo.

   b)  Use the internet to find additional information. Two good sites are Recycle-More at **http://www.recycle-more.co.uk/** and the Recycling Guide at **www.recycling-guide.org.uk**.

   c)  Having collected information, complete your logo.

| Item number and name (e.g. cereal packet) | Number of layers of packaging | Type of packaging (record one tick for each layer of packaging) | | | | | Is the packaging appropriate (✓) or too much (✗)? |
|---|---|---|---|---|---|---|---|
| | | card/paper | plastic film | aluminium foil | plastic | other | |
| 1 | | | | | | | |
| 2 | | | | | | | |
| | | | | | | | |

# E Recycling in the UK

Recycling in the UK has expanded greatly in recent years. Most of us now separate out waste materials at home and have different waste containers. Street refuse collections often involve recycling vehicles with separate containers for paper, card, glass and cans (see Figure 10). Towns now have recycling centres (see Figure 11) where items such as garden waste, hard core (bricks and concrete), oil, clothing and plastics can all be dumped separately and then recycled. Some recycling centres even sell bags of garden compost made from the composted waste garden material!

## Activities

6 Study Figure 10.
   a) What items are being recycled at the recycling centre in the photograph?
   b) The green box is called a container. How has it been designed to help people safely recycle materials?
   c) Containers are easily moved by lorries. Why is this an important consideration?
   d) Notice that the ground is free of all litter and waste (apart from the cardboard boxes about to be recycled). Why is this important?

7 Find out how you recycle at home.
   a) What items do you separate out for recycling? Do you use different containers?
   b) Which items are collected from home?
   c) What happens to the other items?
   d) How often do collections take place from your home?
   e) Are there any other items produced at home that you think could be recycled?
   f) How do you help your family recycle?

▲ Figure 10   Kerbside recycling vehicle

▲ Figure 11   Recycling centre

# F   Made in Britain, dumped in China

The recent boom in recycling in the UK has produced huge amounts of recyclable waste. In 2006, we produced over 7 million tonnes. Increasingly, this waste is being shipped abroad, most notably to China (see Figure 12). In 2006, more than 200,000 tonnes of plastic was exported to China along with 2 million tonnes of used paper and cardboard (see Figure 13). Other items exported to China included large quantities of steel and electrical goods.

Why is our waste going to China? There are two reasons. Firstly, we are producing more recyclable waste than we can cope with. Secondly, China is keen to make use of materials such as plastics to fuel its booming economy. Chinese companies are willing to pay £300 for every tonne of plastic water bottles, whereas UK companies will pay less than £100. It is now cheaper to send plastic to the Far East than by road from London to Manchester!

## ICT ACTIVITY

One of the most important materials recycled is glass. It can be used for a huge range of products and purposes, including artificial sand, bottles, and for arts and crafts. Discover some of the different uses for recycled glass using the internet. A good place to start is British Glass at: **http://www.britglass.org.uk/Education/Recycling.html**. See what you can find and present your information in the form of a table or poster. You could do a similar activity for other materials, such as plastics (chairs, fences, bird feeding boxes, etc.) or rubber (rubber matting, floor tiles, etc.).

## Activity

8  Study Figure 12.

   a) Use an atlas to describe the route taken by ships from the UK to China.

   b) It costs £500 to send a 26-tonne container of plastic from the UK to China. If the plastic sells for £300 a tonne, how much profit will be made from sending a single container to China?

   c) Do you think it is a good idea to send UK waste all the way to China?

   d) What do you think could be done to encourage companies in the UK to use the recyclable waste that we produce?

▼ **Figure 12   Trade of plastic to China**

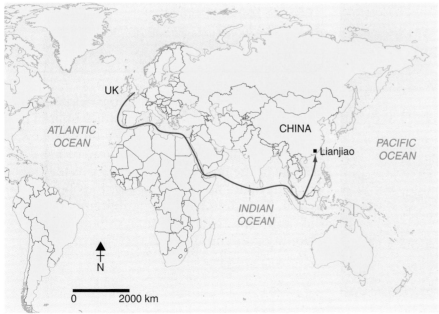

▲ **Figure 13   British plastic waste in China**

## G   Issue: How can aluminium recycling be increased?

When was the last time you had a can of fizzy drink (see Figure 14) or unwrapped the foil package from a chocolate bar? Both have something in common – they are made of aluminium.

Aluminium is a relatively 'soft' metal that can be easily formed into thin wire or rolled into sheets. Many products are made from aluminium because it is very strong yet relatively light. Apart from drinks cans and foil, aluminium is used to make airliners, car engine parts and window-frames. Having many possible uses, it can be described as a very versatile material.

There are several reasons why recycling aluminium is a sensible thing to do.

- Melting used aluminium uses only a fraction (about five per cent) of the electricity used in the original smelting process.

- By using less energy, recycling is good for the environment. It reduces the need to burn fossil fuels thereby cutting the emissions of harmful gases into the atmosphere.

- Aluminium products can be recycled and reused time and time again, without its quality being affected. In this way, once manufactured, it is a largely sustainable material.

▲ **Figure 14   Aluminium drinks can**

### Activity

9   The aim of this activity is to produce a poster to encourage more people to recycle aluminium cans. The poster will be displayed in your school on a 'green' noticeboard, if you have one (if you don't, how about creating one?). Your poster should be informative and attractive, but its main purpose is to increase recycling!

Do some additional research in your school library or on the internet.

Your poster should contain the following details:

- **What is aluminium? Where does it come from and how is it made? Why is it so useful to people?**
- **Why are aluminium products (such as drinks cans) excellent for recycling?**
- **How are drinks cans recycled?**
- **Why should people recycle their drinks cans?**

### Useful websites

**Aluminium Packaging Recycling Organisation (Alupro):**

http://www.alupro.org.uk/index.htm

**DEFRA (for statistics):**

http://www.defra.gov.uk/environment/statistics/waste/index.htm

**The Recycling Guide website at:**

http://www.recycling-guide.org.uk

**Recycle-More website at:**

http://www.recycle-more.co.uk

In 2001, over 5,300,000 aluminium drinks cans were bought in the UK. Whilst over 2 million were recycled, this still left some 3 million cans heading for landfill sites. Aluminium drinks cans are one of the most cost-effective items for recycling. They are relatively easy to collect and to melt down to form 'new' aluminium. One of the challenges for the future is to boost the amount of aluminium cans recycled in the UK.

**Air mass**   large body of air with uniform temperature and humidity

**Arctic**   a type of climate typical of high polar latitudes, often very cold and dry

**Attrition**   a process of river erosion where pebbles bash together to become smaller and more rounded in shape

**Biodegradable**   waste material that will eventually rot down naturally, such as wool.

**Carbonation**   a form of chemical weathering where weak acidic rainwater slowly dissolves limestone or chalk

**Cartographer**   a map maker

**Cavern**   large underground cave often associated with limestone

**Census**   a population survey usually carried out in a country every 10 years. In the UK the next census is in 2011

**Climate**   average weather calculated over a 30-year period

**Climate graph**   a single type of graph that shows rainfall as a bar chart below line graphs showing temperature

**Compass**   an instrument that responds to the Earth's magnetic field and is used to find directions

**Condensation**   the process where water vapour is turned into water droplets forming, for example, cloud

**Confluence**   the point where two rivers join

**Contour**   a line joining points of equal height above sea level

**Desert**   a type of climate with very little rainfall and extremes of temperature

**Distribution**   the spread of, for example, population

**Domestic waste**   waste produced at home, such as paper and waste food

**Economic**   this is a term that relates to money and business

**Economy**   aspects of finance and business

**Ecosystem**   interactions between living organisms and the environment either on a small-scale (e.g. a pond or hedge) or a large-scale (e.g. a desert)

**Emigration**   the movement of people out of a country. Such people are called emigrants

**Energy conservation**   a means of reducing energy use by preventing waste. Double-glazing and loft insulation help to keep heat in the home and reduce the need to use energy

**Erosion**   the sculpting or removal of rocks by natural forces such as rivers

**Estuary**   a wide expanse of water where a river joins the sea

**Farm diversification**   where farmers find alternative ways to make money by, for example, converting an old farm building into a tearoom and farm shop

**Farm system**   a way of organising the activities that take place on a farm. Inputs describe the factors that influence what a farmer does, e.g. the climate. Processes are the activities such as ploughing and harvesting that turn the inputs into outputs (e.g. milk, eggs, straw)

**Floodplain**   a wide flat area of land either side of a river that may become flooded after a period of heavy rain

**Fly tipping**   the illegal dumping of waste, often in the countryside

**Food chain**   links from one source of food to another, for example, grass – rabbit – fox

**Food web**   a diagram showing the links between many organisms often in an ecosystem

**Fossil fuels**   sources of energy formed over millions of years and non-renewable, e.g. coal

**Four-figure grid reference**   a map reference that identifies a grid square

**Freeze-thaw**   a form of physical weathering involving repeated cycles of freezing and thawing of water causing fragments of rock to break away from rock faces

**Geography**   the study of the physical and human patterns and processes on the surface of the Earth

**Global warming**   term applied to the gradual increase in global average temperatures in recent years

# GLOSSARY

**Habitat**  the home of an organism, e.g. a rabbit's burrow

**Hay**  dried grass used in the winter to feed farm animals

**Hazardous waste**  waste that is toxic and dangerous

**Heritage**  evidence of the past, for example, an old building or tree

**Immigrants**  people who have migrated into a country

**Immigration**  the movement of people into a country

**Industrial waste**  waste produced by industry such as polluted water and rock waste

**Inputs**  factors that affect what a farmer does, e.g. climate

**Landfill site**  a large hole or hollow, such as an abandoned quarry, used for the dumping of waste. Nowadays, landfill sites are in short supply and people are being encouraged to reduce, reuse and recycle waste

**Leachate**  liquids produced in landfill sites as rainwater seeps through the waste and dissolves chemicals. It is often toxic and harmful and needs to be treated carefully

**Meander**  a sweeping bend in the course of a river

**Migration**  the movement of people (or birds and animals) from one place to another (e.g. moving house to a better paid job)

**Mixed farm**  farm involved in growing crops and rearing livestock

**Mouth**  the point where a river joins the sea

**Non-biodegradable**  waste that will not rot down naturally, such as tin cans

**Non-renewable energy**  energy from a source that will eventually run out, such as coal or oil

**Outputs**  examples of farm outputs include milk, eggs, straw and bacon

**Pasture**  grassland used for grazing animals, such as cows

**Photosynthesis**  the process in green plants that converts energy from the sun into energy that can be used to feed other organisms

**Polytunnel**  a long plastic-lined tunnel that acts like a greenhouse by creating a warm and sheltered environment for growing crops

**Population density**  the number of people in a certain area, e.g. a square kilometre

**Prevailing wind**  the dominant wind direction. In the UK this is from the southwest

**Primary sector**  jobs that are involved in exploiting a raw material, e.g. coal mining or fishing

**Processes**  actions on a farm that converts inputs to outputs, for example ploughing and harvesting

**Rainshadow**  a relatively dry area often to the leeward (sheltered) side of a range of hills or mountains, e.g. eastern England

**Recycling**  the collection and reuse of common materials such as paper, cardboard and glass. Most households now have recycling collections and many of us use recycled products such as paper

**Reduce**  reducing the amount of waste produced, for example by using reusable bottles or bags

**Relief**  the physical landscape of an area, often referring to height above sea level and slope steepness

**Relief rainfall**  rainfall resulting from moist air being forced to rise, cool and condense over a range of hills or mountains

**Renewable energy**  energy that can be used over and over again, such as water in a hydro-electricity plant or wind

**Reuse**  using a waste resource often for another purpose

**River restoration**  a type of river management that aims to return a river to its original state

**Rush hour**  period of time when a large number of people are travelling to or from work

**Saltation**  the bouncing of sediment on the riverbed

**Scale**   a measure of enlargement or reduction from the original size, often shown as a ratio e.g. 1:50,000

**Scree slope**   a steep slope made up of angular rocks resulting from the process of freeze-thaw

**Secondary sector**   jobs involved in making products such as cars from raw materials

**Silage**   fermented grass used to feed animals in the winter when they cannot graze in pastures

**Site**   the point on the ground where a settlement has been built

**Six-figure grid reference**   a map reference that identifies a point on a map

**Solution**   chemicals dissolved and transported by a river

**Source**   the start of a river

**Spa town**   a town that was or is well known for providing health-giving facilities, e.g. natural springs

**Spot heights**   a precise point measurement of height above sea level

**Stalactite**   a long thin icicle-like deposit of calcite hanging down from the roof of a cavern in limestone rock

**Stalagmite**   a short stumpy deposit of calcium formed on the floor of a cavern by dripping water rich in calcium carbonate

**Standard of living**   a measure of quality of life

**Suspension**   sediment small enough to be carried in the flow of a river

**Sustainable**   a term used to suggest that a resource or feature lasts well into the future without being harmed or damaged by the actions of people. If something is 'sustainable' it will be able to be used and enjoyed by future generations

**Temperate**   a type of climate with moderate temperature and precipitation

**Tertiary sector**   these are jobs in the service sector, such as people working in banks or schoolteachers

**Tidal barrage**   a dam built across a river that holds water back as the tide falls. The water is then channelled through sluice gates in the dam to generate electricity

**Traction**   large sediment rolled along the riverbed

**Tributary**   a small stream that joins a larger river

**Tropical**   a type of climate with high rainfall and high temperatures

**V-shaped valley**   the typical cross profile of a river valley in upland areas

**Waste**   material that is no longer of direct value to the person who has created it. Waste can, however, often be recycled and re-used, such as glass, paper and aluminium. Some waste is biodegradable (e.g. grass cuttings) and will eventually rot down

**Weather**   day to day condition of the atmosphere (e.g. sunshine and rainfall)

**Weathering**   the slow decay or breakdown of rocks in their original position usually involving the weather

**Wildlife corridor**   a strip of natural vegetation (e.g. a hedgerow) that enables organisms to move across a developed landscape (e.g. a ploughed field)

**Wind farm**   a group of several – sometimes hundreds – of individual wind turbines

**Wind turbine**   a modern form of windmill that uses the wind to generate electricity. Wind turbines usually have three blades positioned at the top of a tall tower, which can be turned to face into the wind

**Work/life balance**   a lifestyle that encourages people to balance their working life with time spent resting and playing. Doctors believe that this is a healthy lifestyle

**World Heritage Site**   an internationally important site, such as an historic building or a natural feature, that is protected from future damage and harm